Spiritual Roots of Barley

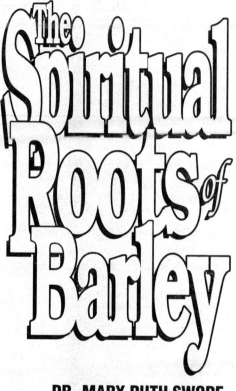

The Spiritual Roots of Barley

DR. MARY RUTH SWOPE
WITH MIRIAM CHAMPNESS

National Preventive Health Services, Inc.
P.O. Box 2236, Melbourne, FL 32902

Copyright © 1988 by **Dr. Mary Ruth Swope**

ISBN 0-936369-24-8

National Preventive Health Services, Inc., publishers

P.O. Box 2236, Melbourne, Florida, 32902

*Distributed through Nutrition With a Mission,
P.O. Box 1746, Melbourne, FL 32902*

Library of Congress Cataloguing in Publication Data

Printed in the United States of America

Unless otherwise noted, Scripture quotations are taken from the *King
James Version of the Holy Bible.*

Scripture quotations marked (AMP) or so designated in the text are
from the *Amplified Bible.* Old Testament copyright © 1965, 1987 by
the Zondervan Corporation. The Amplified New Testament
copyright © 1958, 1987 by the Lockman Foundation. Used by
permission.

Scripture quotations marked (NIV) are from the *Holy Bible, New
International Version,* copyright © 1973, 1978, 1984 International
Bible Society. Used by permission of Zondervan Bible Publishers.

Scripture quotations marked (TLB) are from *The Living Bible.*
Copyright ©1971 by Tyndale House Publishers, Wheaton Illinois.
Used by permission.

Scripture quotations marked (JB) are from *The Jerusalem Bible,*
copyright ©1966, 1967 and 1968 by Darton, Longman & Todd Ltd.
and Doubleday & Co., Inc. Used by permission.

Contents

Acknowledgments

I wish to express my deep appreciation to God for putting me in touch with Christians in California, Oregon, North Dakota and Florida who gave me personal insights into the "spiritual roots" of barley beyond that of my own understanding.

Too, I appreciate the rather miraculous way in which Miriam Champness came into my life at the precise moment I needed help in finishing this companion book to the volume, *GREEN LEAVES OF BARLEY: A Food with Real Power.* I could tell she was heaven-sent when I gave her a handful of "rough pebbly stones" and she returned them to me as a skillfully polished, highly readable text.

Another friend, Julie Frahm, displayed keen insight as she joined me in seeking true *rhema* regarding the spiritual references to barley and the production of this book.

May it please God to use these our efforts to increase your understanding of and appreciation for the spiritual roots of barley.

A Special Word to the Reader

"What," you may ask, "is a nutrition educator doing writing a book on the SPIRITUAL ROOTS of something, even if it is barley? Isn't that the province of the theologian or one trained in religion?"

Yes, of course it is, and I am neither! Therefore, the biblical explorations of the significance of barley which you will find in this book are not any kind of an attempt at theology.

But for those of you who find "intuitive theologies" in some of the statements, let me declare my heartfelt conviction: God is perfect in all His ways and His Word is true. If anything I say seems to stray from that truth, it is my error; please blow it away with a breath of kindness.

Let me make another basic statement. I am using the word "spiritual" in relation to barley to express what I have come to believe is the life principle, the real meaning, the true intention, the divine animating influence of barley as a food for man and animals on earth.

At no time in using the word "spiritual" in application to barley, in any form, am I linking it to either Christian salvation or to the occult. Salvation comes from God who alone has the power to cleanse and purify the spirit of man, and according to the Scriptures, is available only through faith in His Son, Jesus Christ and His atoning blood. (The occult, of course, is totally foreign to my beliefs).

Having said what I am not attempting, let me tell you the two major purposes at the heart of this book. The first is to glorify God by promoting a deeper understanding of His marvelous providence in creating barley. The second is to stir up in the heart of the reader a hunger for His Word and a desire to find further light from the Scriptures in this area.

The early researches for this were done before I knew a book would evolve from my studies. They were simply the results of my seeking God's perfect will for me in regard to further involvement with the distribution of Barley Green, that powerful food concentrate derived as dried juice from young leaves of the barley plant.

To these findings, I am pleased to add the insights and researches of several other Christians who were prompted to share with me on the topic of barley. We made generous use of Bible dictionaries, con-

cordances, commentaries, and even Jewish encyclopedias as aids to our understanding of the Scriptures.

The result is a volume of personal insights gained
through seeking God's point of view in regard to
barley. It is my prayer that we were accurate in our
reading and interpretation of God's Word and that
this book will bring you wisdom and blessing.

Foreword

There are many people who have a deep interest in the science of nutrition but little or none in understanding the relationship of spiritual health to physical health.

On the other hand, there are people who have a passionate interest in spiritual matters who have little or no interest in nutrition as a way of promoting physical health and longevity.

In an effort to appeal to both these groups, I have written two different books on essentially the same subject. Although they are written from different points of view, both books seek to arouse interest in the dried raw juice of the embryonic leaves of the barley plant. This is because I believe that matters of nutrition involving both physical health and spiritual health are related at a deep level, and green barley is an important focus of that concern. As a nutrition educator of nearly 50 years of study and experience, I see this little-known new food (it has been on our market since April 1982) as the single most exciting ray of nutritional hope that I know of for an overfed yet undernourished America.

I have come to believe strongly what the scientist who pioneered this new food has to say about it: "It is the most prolific source of nutrients in a balanced form in a single food on the face of the earth."

Therefore, it came as no surprise to me that a closer examination of the biblical references to barley revealed it as a God-given answer to our physical needs, provided from the beginning by Christ, our Creator, whose very nature is revealed in its healing provision. If I could have just one nutritional wish come true it would be that every man, woman and child in this nation take advantage of this providential way to improve energy and health at the cellular level by consuming daily an appropriate amount of dried green barley juice.

My new book *GREEN LEAVES OF BARLEY: A Food with Real Power* deals only with the physical and chemical properties of dried barley juice and was written to answer questions from those whose primary interest is in physical health through good nutrition. *The Spiritual Roots of Barley*, on the other hand, is written primarily for readers who would have an interest in understanding the scriptural references to barley. It grew out of my study of these, and especially my desire to understand why God chose barley leaves as the *wave offering* to be presented annually at the Jewish Festival of Firstfruits (see Leviticus 23:11-13).

As my desire for deeper scriptural understanding of barley grew, I was led to books and people whose help was indispensable. The deeper meaning of the biblical stories involving barley grain, barley loaves, and barley leaves began to unfold with interesting, even intriguing overtones. The awesome power of God's intricately interwoven plan for us became ever clearer.

Barley truly has deep spiritual meaning, a glimpse of which I share with you in this little book.

CHAPTER ONE

PROVISION:

What's So Special About Barley?

Not even once while I was pushing an old-fashioned, hand-driven lawn mower over our large lawn in my youth did I question the history of grass. Where did it come from? How long had it been here? What was its significance? I just knew my parents had said that it was my turn to mow the grass. And I did!

All of that changed, of course, after I learned about Barley Green — the food concentrate made from the tender young leaves of barley grass. This live, naturally potent, organically-grown product led me into a study of the grasses and grains that held my fascinated attention for months.

Being a believer who respects the authority of Scripture, I went there first for information. Chapter

1 of Genesis provided a foundational insight into the answers to my questions. In verses 11-12, I read:

> *"And God said, Let the earth bring forth grass, the herb yielding seed, and the fruit tree yielding fruit after his kind, whose seed is in itself, upon the earth, and it was so. And the earth brought forth grass, and herb yielding seed after his kind, and the tree yielding fruit, whose seed was in itself, and God saw that it was good."*

This miracle took place in the third day of Creation. A little further on, in Genesis 1:29, God speaks directly to Adam and Eve.

> *"And God said, Behold I have given you every herb bearing seed, which is upon the face of all the earth, and every tree, in the which is the fruit of a tree yielding seed; to you it shall be for meat."*

In these verses we find the groundwork for the concepts that I have come to call the "spiritual roots" of barley. For barley is indeed a grass, along with all the cereal grains (wheat, oats, rye, rice, etc.), and botanically grasses are classified as herbs. All seed-bearing green plants that die off at the end of each growing season are herbs, and within that category, grass is the largest and most numerous family of green plants on this earth.

THE PRIMACY OF GRASSES

My interest was immediately sparked by the order in which God calls these, the first of all living things, into being. First grass, then all the other herbs, then the woody species. Why is grass first, and what does that tell us about barley? I have come to believe that this *primacy* or firstness is the central root from which all the other spiritual roots of barley can be derived. Let me explain.

The grasses seem to have a very special place in the plan of creation. In his book, *This World of Wonder,* naturalist Hal Borland deals with the crucial role of the grasses in the realm of nature:

> *"We are more dependent on grass than on any other species of plant life. We could live without trees.*
>
> *We could do without the beautiful flowering plants, but without grass we would starve. We would have neither bread nor meat.*
>
> *All cereal grains are grasses .... All our meat animals ... eat grass in some form. Grass also anchors the earth's soil against erosion and helps check floods. Grass cools the earth and the air and is constantly renewing the oxygen in the air we breathe.*
>
> *Grass grows almost everywhere, except in the deepest woodland and the driest desert. It flourishes wherever there is soil and moisture and a few weeks of summer warmth.*
>
> *(It) is so insistent and so efficient in sprouting and growing that it outnumbers all other plants.*
>
> *Nearly all plants are able to renew themselves after being cut or broken off, but grass is outstand-*

*ing in this ability. Break off or cut one stem and
another stem soon grows to take its place."* [1]

In this profile of the grasses, we begin to see some
of God's design considerations in creating grass first:
its roots hold everything together! It is the foundation of the entire food chain, as well as playing a
crucial role in cleansing the entire atmosphere; it is
incredibly persistent, and has an almost miraculous
power of renewal.

In fact, grass is the plant that springs up everywhere there is earth, whether we plant it or not. It is
unstoppable — just about indestructible!

This idea can be confirmed by every person who
has had any experience with gardening. Just when
you think you have your plot cultivated to perfection
— nothing in sight but beautiful earth — a few days
later, you walk by and what do you see? **Grass**! God
has improved on your perfection!!

I believe God meant for the grasses to be impos-
sible to eradicate. You can even plow a piece of
ground to eight inches in depth, turning it over and
uprooting everything in it, and it will still come up
grass within a few weeks. As a member of the grass
family, barley shows this same remarkable potency.
In the form of green barley concentrate, this potency
becomes available to you and me as we make it part
of our daily diet.

I have come to believe, and I hope I can show you

why, that barley grass has a special place in God's
plan. It is a food packed with both biochemical
power and spiritual significance, as we will dis-
cover. I believe God has used its marvelous potency
from the beginning to provide protection from disease and for the perfecting of our physical health.

As one medical doctor said not too long ago,
"Clearly, Green Barley boosts the immune system. It
provides powerful support for the body's own health-
promoting mechanisms." From all of this it shouldn't
surprise us to read that archaeologists have found
evidence indicating that barley may have been the
first cereal grass cultivated by mankind.[2]

THE PRIMACY OF BARLEY

Not only was barley the grass that was among the
first of the green plants created, according to the
Genesis record, but it is also first in another very
important way. The biblical record for this root is
Leviticus 23:10-12.

> "Speak unto the children of Israel, and say unto
> them, When ye be come into the land which I give
> unto you, and shall reap the harvest thereof, then ye
> shall bring a sheaf of the firstfruits of your harvest
> unto the priest: And he shall wave the sheaf before
> the Lord, to be accepted for you: on the morrow
> after the sabbath the priest shall wave it."

In this chapter, Moses is receiving very specific

instructions from the Lord God Jehovah. He is in charge of setting up an entirely new thing on the face of the earth, the first nation to be governed by laws directly from God.

Moses' instructions in this 23rd chapter of Leviticus are in the area of sacrifices to be offered to God in thanksgiving for deliverance and providence. He is told to instruct the priests to take a sheaf of the first crop to ripen in Israel every year and to wave it before the Lord as a sacrifice of thanksgiving. God promises that through that sacrifice, he will find the Israelites acceptable in His sight.

That sheaf from the first crop to ripen every year was made up of the leaves and fruits of barley. To this very day the nation of Israel presents a sheaf of barley to the Lord at the Feast of the Firstfruits. I think it is fascinating to see how Scripture witnesses to the primacy of barley in several different ways. We will study this particular aspect more deeply in Chapter Two.

As I see it, the principle of primacy is the heart of the matter. Just as Jesus is **First** spiritually, with all the power and authority that implies, I believe the Lord made barley to ripen **First** in the natural realm with provision for bringing our earthly bodies into line with God's perfect will for our healing and health.

From this principle of primacy come other spiritual roots of barley: provision and power, protection and perfection. You will find a chapter on each of these themes as we journey together in search of the spiritual dimensions of barley found in God's Word.

GRASSES IN THE PLAN OF CREATION

We have begun to look at the spiritual roots of the grasses, that is, their purpose and essential meaning in God's design.

What God said about the green plants, including herbs and grasses, was **"To you they shall be for meat."** In other words, they are for our sustenance; we are to use them for food and to sustain life. The psalmist in Psalm 104:14 praises God for creating "herbs for the service of man: that he may bring forth food out of the earth." Not only are we to eat them, but their purpose is to serve us and to make it possible for us to do our work, to survive!

A further meaning of the word "herb" is: a green plant found over the ages to have **curative** powers. The word "curative" comes from a Latin word which means "to take care of." We use it interchangeably with the word "remedy," and certainly there are many books on the subject of herbs which show that specific herbs may be used *to take care of* or *remedy* specific ailments or deficiencies. It is my belief that barley grass falls naturally into that category. The many testimonies that we receive certainly add credence to this idea.

As of this writing, the U.S. Food and Drug Administration has ruled out all claims of curative powers for herbs (and most products not manufactured by a drug company). So you will not find such claims here. They cannot, however, change the dictionary definition of herb or the history of humankind, both of which bear witness to that property of herbs which is now illegal to state as fact in a public forum.

Perhaps it is just as well, however, that herbs cannot be confused with medicine, which, in this country at this point in time, usually means *drugs*. For the potency of the herbs, such as barley grass, comes from a completely different principle. The green leaves of live plants were meant to restore and renew the human system by enhancing the natural, God-designed functioning of that system. (See Ezekiel 47:12 and Revelation 22:2.)

Drugs, on the other hand, intervene in the human system to kill germs or manipulate some particular body process or another. Of course, it is not always their purpose to cause disruption in the natural functioning of the human body; but in many cases they do. So, we might say that herbs, unlike drugs, do not **cure**; instead, they **enhance health** as God intended them to do in the overall master design of creation.

GOD'S HEALTH PLAN

Being the Creator, God knew what many seem to have forgotten or ignored: that He designed all creatures with self-renewing systems that work perfectly, but **only when supplied with nutrition according to His plan**. It is clear that His plan was for us to eat a varied selection of grains, nuts, seeds, legumes, fruits and vegetables.

Within each of these categories God has purposefully provided a wide variety of nutrients. In vegetables, for example, the part we eat may be the leaf, stem, flower, fruit, seed, tuber, bulb or root. Surely God's supply of food is as "fearfully and wonderfully made" as are the ones for whom it was created!

We tend to think of food as primarily fuel—like gasoline in a car. But a closer look reveals God designed food for three purposes: besides supplying energy for action, food becomes part of our bodies as it is used to build tissue; it is also intended to maintain the organism by regulating a myriad of body processes in the cells, tissues and organs throughout life.

Thus, our cells are actually built up (or torn down) by the food we eat, digest, and assimilate. In fact, the very processes of life are regulated by the organic chemicals found in food. **Fresh** food and **pure** water are, of course, the best sources of these.

It is the complex process of maintenance that actually results in healing and renewal if it is allowed to proceed without hindrance. When God created us from the "dust of the earth," he provided for that

renewal process by giving us **food from the earth**
that contained all the nutrients needed for renewal.

Being a perfect God, He designed barley perfectly to accomplish these purposes. He knew that
our bodies would maintain themselves in an ongoing state of health if we obeyed His instructions
about what to put (and what **not** to put) into them.
We will see that His instructions include a strong
emphasis on barley as part of His health plan.

I believe we still have the power of that design
available. And I believe I can show from Scripture
that He intended us to use barley grass for both
health and healing, for the two were inseparable in
His plan.

MISSING GOD'S PLAN

Modern food marketing has resulted in our eating
less and less of the **food from the earth** required for
the God-given process of growth, maintenance and
renewal. Then, once our bodies begin to show the
obvious results of poor nutrition (sickness and degenerative disease), we find ourselves taking pre-
scribed synthetic chemicals, which we call "medicine." These may handle our symptoms but may not
actually restore us to health.

Ask yourself how God's design for health and
healing through renewal can proceed unhindered if
we ignore the foods we're instructed to feed on in
our User's Manual (Holy Scripture), and insist on

loading our systems instead with substances they were never designed to handle.

The Bible shows us that **not** following God's plan always has its price. King Solomon of Israel showed deep wisdom when he wrote about the consequences of "having our own way." The Living Bible says:

> *"For you closed your eyes to the facts and did not choose to reverence and trust the Lord, and you turned your back on me (wisdom), spurning my advice. That is why you must eat the bitter fruit of having your own way, and experience the full terrors of the pathway you have chosen" (Prov. 1:29-31).*

I receive many letters each week from people who are bedfast or in wheelchairs, or on total disability at an early age. They are suffering from many different diseases, often the results of "having their own way" in regard to diet. Nutritional ignorance can be "hazardous to your health!" So can making wrong choices. A word to the wise is still sufficient.

So why do we lavish our grasses and grains (and particularly barley) on livestock, then load up on animal foods and synthetic substances? Should it really surprise us when we end up victims of degenerative diseases that would never have plagued us in the first place if we had followed God's plan? How then shall we recover from the nutritional crisis we have brought about by neglecting God's advice on how to eat?

Well, in any event, let's not look for sound nutritional counsel from those who make millions every year from our collective lack of nutritional knowledge. For sound nutritional counsel and Godly wisdom, let's turn to the Lord who made heaven and earth — the one who designed our bodies and understands our metabolisms!

REDISCOVERING NATURAL HEALTH

Of course, it was the Lord Himself who invented **whole person medicine** and healing. But just in the last couple of decades, we have seen the concept of herbs and health brought to the fore again by a handful of hardy pioneers in the field of natural health.

Although the majority consider them *health nuts*, and the medical and pharmaceutical establishment do all they can to discredit them, these people cannot all be labeled fanatics. They are, for the most part, people for whom the present-day regimen of meat-three-times-a-day, processed food and synthetic drugs **simply did not work**. Looking for alternatives, they researched the medical record of past generations and *even* studied nutrition as a way to health. In their search for wisdom, some discovered God's Word and found new life both spiritually and physically!

Those who followed this search for alternatives

have been known for years to eat such things as alfalfa sprouts and drink juice of newly sprouted grains. They've been joined by a small number of courageous preventive-health-minded doctors.

It took a Japanese medical doctor with a background in pharmaceutical research to produce scientific evidence that they were on the right track. Dr. Yoshihide Hagiwara and his colleagues have generated a growing body of evidence for the health-giving properties of the grasses and leafy green vegetables, and most particularly of barley grass.

It was Dr. Hagiwara who invented a method of processing the juice of barley grass sprouts that retains all the live nutrients intact and keeps them that way for a shelf life of three years. This is the product available in America as "Barley Green." (At this present writing, several new American-produced products are also available).

When we consider the nutritional status of a nation so *civilized* that it gets harder every day to find God's kind of food (fresh from the earth), it is easy to see why I consider barley concentrates God's new provision for us who live in a veritable dietary wasteland. Jehovah Jireh, our Provider, has done it again!

PRACTICAL TRUTHS ABOUT BARLEY

Since many readers may not have read my earlier book *GREEN LEAVES OF BARLEY; A Food With*

Real Power, before reading this book, I want to introduce you to some practical truths that interested me as I studied about barley.

I believe God's providence is clearly seen in these facts.

• In our country barley is sown in November and is harvested in April.

• Barley is the first grain to ripen in the spring; wheat is next and it takes 4-6 weeks longer to mature.

• It ripens without the aid of all of the "latter rains." This has significance and will be referred to later.

• Its vibrant growth offered the ancient people, especially, a new sign … of new life in the spring — a sign of hope.

• It brought a new taste appeal to the meals of the ancient people whose winter diets were often meager in both types and amounts of food.

• The barley crop was a revelation of God's faithfulness; His immutable ways were displayed in each year's new crops.

• It grew wild for hundreds of years and was plentiful; it was also plentiful after it became a cultivated crop.

• Barley was cheap to buy; everyone could afford it.

• It is hardy; it thrives in high altitudes and northern climatic conditions. It resists disease.

• It is not attacked by bugs, molds, fungi, or worms, which abound later and in warmer climates.

• It is thought to be the first cereal cultivated by man. Grains found in Egypt have been tagged as 5,000 years old.

• Regrettably, in America 65 percent is used in animal feed and another large proportion goes into brewing beer and ale.[3]

BRINGING HEALTH INTO FOCUS THROUGH GREEN BARLEY

You can find a complete nutritional profile of the dried juice from young barley leaves in Chapter 2 of *GREEN LEAVES OF BARLEY*. My purpose here is to give you a brief overview of the nutritional value of young, raw, "alive" green leaves of the barley plant — the "aristocrat" of plants and the granddaddy of all cereals. What follows is a brief **guided tour** of the special properties designed into green barley leaves by our omniscient Creator.

ALKALINITY

In understanding the outstanding qualities of green barley leaves as a food with power, let us begin with its virtue as an alkaline food. To understand alkalinity, you need to understand the symbol "pH" which is the measurement used to express the ratio between acids and alkalines in our body fluids. The scale indicates acidity from 0 to 7.0 and alkalinity from 7.0 to 14.0.

Barley grows very well in alkaline soil, so it comes as no surprise that the green leaves of barley test, in the laboratory, as one of the most alkaline of all natural foods. Spinach is its next rival in alkalinity but is only about 40 percent as alkaline as Barley Green, for example.

It is well-known in medical circles that many diseases thrive in an acid medium; only a few can survive an alkaline pH. Recently an M.D. made the statement that the pH of the average American is 5.4 instead of the ideal 7.35-7.45. Why is this?

Our systemic acid condition may be attributed to our high intake of meat (beef, pork, veal, chicken, turkey, etc.), high sugar and soft-drink consumption and excessive consumption of preserved foods.

This puts us outside of God's design for our optimal functioning. Many Americans are plagued, therefore, with unhealthy bodies due to this.

To further illustrate the effect of pH, the doctor referred to above also stated in his speech that cancer cells definitely will not live in a pH that is 5.7 or higher. If that is really true, and I have no reason to doubt his scholarship, then many of you may be interested in checking the pH of your system. For those who wish to do so, I have included this information that may be of help to readers.

An easy way to test your body's pH, according to Dr. Jack Soltanoff, is as follows:

"You can check the pH balance of your body by dipping a two-inch strip of Nitrazene paper into your saliva and another into your urine. (Both are necessary to get an accurate reading). In only a few seconds, the paper will turn a color that you can match to one of seven shades indicating your acid/alkaline balance. You can buy this inexpensive paper in any drugstore. Similar to a thermometer or a scale, the pH check is a way of monitoring your body's health.

"Be sure you do this at night before retiring (before brushing your teeth) and also in the morning after you wake up (before brushing your teeth). (If you check after a meal, the pH simply reflects the food you've just eaten)." [4]

Because the juice of young barley leaves is so effective in neutralizing our acid pH balance, a teaspoonful or two a day is a healthful habit to establish.

We are truly blessed to have food concentrates-made from barley leaves to aid our systems in returning to the proper pH for ongoing good health.

CHLOROPHYLL

One of the most powerful components of dried barley juice is its rich chlorophyll content. Chlorophyll is the green color in plants and is designed to function as the BLOOD of the plant. Without chlorophyll there would be no plants and without plants there would be no animal life on earth, including us!

Based upon research study conclusions, chlorophyll is shown to be effective in treating anemia, bad breath, and all body odors — even those caused by colostomies, severe burns, bone infections, perspiration, etc.

Chlorophyll has also proven to be a wound healer, a help in eye, ear, nose and throat problems, in chronic sinus and ulcer cases and many more. It was shown to be the most effective of 11 different agents (including sulfa drugs, penicillin, etc.) in healing bed sores.

Lastly, chlorophyll seems to provide specific help in allergies and inflammatory diseases like arthritis. The way it does this is still in the realm of mystery to scientists. Nonetheless, thousands testify that their health has been restored through the inclusion of daily servings of green barley concentrate.

ENZYMES

One of the unique characteristics of dried barley leaves is their hundreds of **LIVE** enzymes. Until you understand the significance of this, you cannot appreciate either health or healing!

A good way to help you understand the importance of enzymes is by giving you an illustration. An architect, in cooperation with a contractor, may determine every item of material needed for building a new home. These hundreds of items could be correctly ordered and safely delivered to a building site. But until the carpenters, brick layers, plasterers, painters and other *specialists* come to do the work, the home remains unbuilt. **Enzymes** are the workers for putting the house together!

Enzymes are the body's *labor force* in performing all chemical and biological processes in the body. We are born with a given, limited amount of enzyme activity; we must learn how to conserve it.

Depleting our enzyme supply results in a weakened immune system. Weakening our immune system makes us prime targets for cancer, heart disease, arthritis, diabetes, AIDS, allergies and a whole host of other degenerative diseases.

Some of the best news about green barley leaves is in the presence of several dynamic enzymes. These particular enzymes neutralize poisons, resolve all sorts of cancer-causing petroleum-based nitro compounds, strengthen the body to resist and counteract mutations (damaged cells which can cause birth defects, cancer etc.), heal ulcers and other inflammatory lesions — and that is only a partial list!

Most importantly, one enzyme in dried barley juice is known to stimulate the repair of DNA, the genetic material involved in birth defects and cancers. Recent research also confirms that certain enzymes in barley leaves help the body to maintain youthful characteristics.

Those whose diet is high in enzymes seem to experience increased vitality and are relatively free from degenerative diseases. The body's immune system can be greatly strengthened by the addition of live enzymes, and many symptoms of sickness and disease respond to increasing the amount of live (raw) food in the diet, with all its natural enzymes.[5]

PROTEIN

Young barley leaves are an excellent source of all the essential amino acids. (From these the body can make all of the other amino acids.) According to Dr. Hagiwara, Barley Green is more than 40 percent protein by weight, which is about 90 percent usable. To give you a source of comparison, a hamburger is about 20-22 percent protein and it has the added disadvantage of being 40 percent or more of fat with cholesterol-building properties in addition.

Many Americans seem to have the wrong idea about protein. In their minds is the idea that we need MEAT to grow "big muscles" with "great strength" and "great endurance" — ability to work long hours at hard jobs and without much fatigue. This is not at all true. Plant proteins are excellent at achieving the above goals as long as they are properly combined and consumed at the same meal. For example, rice and beans make a protein that will achieve the same body functions as meat, if eaten in the right quantities.

Many studies have shown that vegetarian diets which incorporate adequate amounts of grains, legumes, nuts, sprouts, etc., produce healthy people. The biblical story of Daniel is a good one to illustrate this. He and his three friends refused to eat the king's food. After three years of a vegetarian diet with only water to drink, the king said of these four youths:

"And in all matters requiring information and balanced judgment, the king found these young men's advice ten times better than that of all the skilled magicians and wise astrologers in his realm" (Daniel 1:20, TLB).

In recent years, the nine-year study of Seventh-day Adventists done at Loma Linda University comparing these vegetarians with an equal number of the general population of California who were omnivores showed the Adventists significantly ahead of the other group in every test. They had less degenerative disease and were more productive in their work.[8] Vegetable proteins **are** well utilized by the body and have the added advantage of adding **no** fat and **no** cholesterol to the diet. That is another reason I am excited about the green leaves of barley as a food concentrate.

VITAMINS AND MINERALS

Green barley leaves provide a wide spectrum of vitamins and minerals in a balanced form, making it a significant source of these essential nutrients for good health. The amounts of these substances at first glance are not impressive. Americans have become so accustomed to the megadose amounts in synthetic products, that by contrast, the nutrients in green barley concentrates look like "wind pudding and air sauce" — of no significance whatever.

Do not be deceived. The body needs only infinitesimal amounts of minerals and vitamins to carry out all of its functions perfectly — when provided in the right form and balance. Fresh, natural food is, of course, the best source; a food concentrate like green barley with its low-temperature processing is another. Possibly an area of future study in medicine will be how to correct the conditions created by the intake of excessively high amounts of synthetic vitamins and minerals.

THE SPIRITUAL ROOTS OF BARLEY

From this review of some of the major components in barley leaves, could we conclude they are one of the most valuable of all crops for human and animal nutrition? Again, I say I believe so. To my mind, the powder made from the juice of embryonic leaves of the barley plant is **nutritional dynamite**.

That is why I consider it perfectly appropriate to study the *spiritual roots* of barley: its design, purposes and essential meaning in God's master plan. Barley leaves offer mankind a source not only of provision, but of power, protection and perfection. The next few chapters will help you better understand why I call these concepts **"the spiritual roots of barley."**

FOOTNOTES

[1] Hal Borland, *This World of Wonder,* Lippincott Co., Philadelphia, PA, 1973, p. 27.

[2] Samuel Matz, Cereal Science, AVI Publishing Co. Inc., Westport, CT, 1959, p. 97.

[3] Ibid.

[4] Jack Soltanoff, D.C., *Natural Healing,* Warner Books, New York, NY., 1988, p. 21.

[5] Howell, Edward, *Enzyme Nutrition,* Avery Publishing Group, Inc., Wayne NJ., 1985.

CHAPTER TWO

PERFECTION:
Barley, Type of the Perfect Sacrifice

Anyone with a nutritional science background can look at the analysis of green barley leaves and be amazed at the near-perfect balance among the nutrients. But as a Christian, my desire was to understand the biochemical structure and function of this food within the context of God's overall design, for only then would the essential purpose of its nearly perfect configuration come into true perspective.

You can imagine how excited I was when the dimension of perfection was revealed, on closer study, to be one of the basic themes in the scriptural references to barley!

From the beginning of Israel's history as a nation and right down to this very day, barley is the sheaf used as the Offering of the Firstfruits in the Feast of the Passover. Of course, the basic requirement of an offering is that it be "perfect, without spot or stain." Barley, due to its early maturation, is almost completely free of the pests and infestations other crops are plagued with. Thus, it is *naturally perfect.*

In fact, we find barley used in the New Testament as a "type" or prophetic image of Jesus Christ, the one truly perfect sacrifice. In order to understand this concept better, we need to study a little about the Jewish feasts. I have much to share with you on this topic, but let me begin with another personal experience.

SEEKING FOR TRUTH

When I was first introduced to Barley Green and was seeking God's will in the matter of becoming involved in distributing it, I had a very meaningful experience one day while I was praying. I believe God's Holy Spirit gave me a special understanding about barley leaves that I would like to share with you.

I was reading the Bible one morning, as is my regular habit. In Leviticus 23:9-11, I read,

> *"And the Lord spake unto Moses, saying, Speak unto the children of Israel, and say unto them, When ye be come into the land which I give unto you, and shall reap the harvest thereof, then ye shall*

bring a sheaf of the firstfruits of your harvest unto the priest: And he shall wave the sheaf before the Lord, to be accepted for you: on the morrow after the sabbath the priest shall wave it."

Those words seemed to leap right off the page, and I knew in my heart there was a special significance to them for my personal situation. I knew I was to investigate every possible avenue of insight.

As I began researching that passage in the Jewish historical books, Jewish encyclopedias and other reference works, the words came alive. I knew more and more deeply that there is special spiritual significance in barley — for it is barley that ripens first every year and was the sheaf used in ancient times, and to this very day, to celebrate the Festival of the Firstfruits, part of the Feast of the Passover.

I knew in my spirit that God had a special reason for making barley the first crop and giving it a special place in the worship celebrations of Israel; so I continued to read and to seek for the rich inner meanings I was sure God had in store for me. His Word says true seekers are guaranteed finders (Matthew 7:7).

THE MEANING OF THE FIRSTFRUITS

Soon after this, during my daily quiet time, I was pondering in my spirit what I had been learning about barley as firstfruits. I began to look at some other scriptures on firstfruits. My concordance led me to this verse in 1 Corinthians 15:20:

> *"But now is Christ risen from the dead, and become the firstfruits of them that slept."*

Now I began to get really excited! It was clear that there was a spiritual principle here, if I could just grasp it. Through this prophetic image, Scripture links the firstfruits, barley, with our Savior, Jesus Christ. I knew that the primary reason for this was to highlight the perfection and firstness of the one and only truly perfect sacrifice on our behalf. But I also prayed that the Holy Spirit would give me deeper understanding: what did this tell me about barley?

Could it be God means for barley to operate as a *savior* in the physical realm? I looked up "savior" and found it defined as "something that is a means, cause, or source of preservation."[1] That certainly fit with the experiences recorded by the people who turned to green barley after having been told there was nothing further medicine could do for them.

Next in thought came the words, "What Jesus is to the spirit, barley leaves are to the body." I grabbed my pen and wrote it down. The first word that came to my mind after writing that was, of course, "savior." Quickly following came the others — healer, redeemer, provider, deliverer, protector, my strength...they just welled up within me as I gave thanks for this understanding.

Since that day, I have discovered more exciting reasons why we as Christians must understand the principles behind the offering of the firstfruits in order to operate in everything God has for us.

One fact to remember as you read about these principles is that Jesus Christ is the only way to spiritual perfection. Mankind has certainly tried every other way, but Jesus is The Way provided by God, and He is the way that works. God asks us to be perfect, and He graciously provides The Way to become perfect — not in our own strength, but through an ever-increasing reliance on Him.

The same is true, I believe, with barley on the physical level. God asks for our bodies as a living sacrifice, holy and acceptable unto Him (Romans 12:1). And He provides the way to perfect our earthly bodies — through the food that He gave from the beginning of time for that very purpose.

It is with a sense of great anticipation I share with you what I have discovered. My prayer is that it will not only bless you but excite you spiritually. I know there is a deep vein of spiritual riches here—perhaps you will be the next one to come up with a precious gem of spiritual understanding to share with others.

'FIRSTFRUITS OF THEM THAT SLEPT'

Let us begin with Jesus, knowing we will also return to Him, as all things have their beginning and ending in Him. The New Testament has seven references to "firstfruits," of which two verses have particular significance for our study. The first one is in 1 Corinthians 15:20. This is what we looked at before: "But now is Christ risen from the dead, and become the firstfruits of them that slept."

But God goes even farther than that and declares US "firstfruits" in the letter from James, "He chose to give us birth through the word of truth, that we might be a kind of firstfruits of all he created." (James 1:18, NIV).

This makes good spiritual sense to us, as we remember the words of Jesus Christ in His prayer for His own in John the 15th chapter and fourth verse:

"Abide in me, and I in you."

If we are in Christ Jesus, we are called to be an offering of firstfruits, just as He is.

'BLESSED, HAPPY, AND FORTUNATE'

Now, I wish I had every one of you in a classroom where I would be the teacher. I would ask for a show of hands on these questions: "Have you ever heard a sermon or a lecture on the feasts of Israel as described in both the Old and the New Testaments? Have you ever read a book on the subject? Do you know anything at all about them?"

Except for my Jewish students, I imagine there would be almost no hands extended in answer to those questions. Our education on such matters has

been, for the most part, woefully inadequate. Somehow we have never been taught some of the most
beautiful and useful lessons in all of Scripture.

I repeat here a verse from the Bible in the Amplified translation that says what I now feel and want to
share with you:

> *"Blessed — happy, fortunate [To be envied] —
> are the people who know the joyful sound [who
> understand and appreciate the spiritual blessing
> symbolized by the feasts]; they walk, O Lord, in the
> light and favor of Your countenance!" (Psalm
> 89:15).*

Let us begin, then, our primary education in the
feasts of Israel so we may respond to God's will for
His firstfruits people.

THE FEASTS OF ISRAEL

There are three major feasts of the Lord in Israel,
with a total of seven celebrations within the three. At
each of these feasts, Passover, Pentecost, and Tabernacles, God commanded all Israel to come together
before Him. They are still celebrated in Israel today.
Here are some general facts about all the feasts:

• They are God's idea — not man's; and God
expects obedience from every participant.

• God wants to meet man on His terms, to accomplish His purposes in their lives.

• The times and seasons for the feasts are very

specific and unvarying, as are the directions for the specific celebrations and sacrifices in each feast.

• These are holy days, a time for renewed commitment to a holy life, renouncing sin, idolatry, and immorality.

• Gentiles can attend, but only if they are believers. This is a time of solidarity for the Israel of God. Aliens and strangers are not welcome.

• Offering of Firstfruits was a part of each feast:

Passover: the firstfruits of barley are offered at barley harvest in the Spring.

Pentecost: the firstfruits of wheat are offered 50 days after Passover.

Tabernacles: the firstfruits of orchard and vineyard are offered in the fall of the year.

• Every feast represents the earthly counterpart to a specific mighty act of God:

Passover: the deliverance of Israel from Egypt.
Pentecost: the giving of the law.
Tabernacles: the taking of the promised land with thanksgiving for deliverance and provision; the rededication of Israel to God (Day of Atonement).

I believe that what the Lord was really looking for in **all** these feasts and offerings was a people that would acknowledge that He was their Lord and their God and that they were willing to obey Him even to the smallest detail.

He still desires that in us today as we receive His sacrifice in Jesus and obey the Holy Spirit's urging to "grow up" in Christ and to walk like Jesus did. How did He walk? He listened to the Father and then did what the Father told Him to do.

It doesn't take a lot of education or a big ministry or loads of money — God often uses the weakest and most imperfect of us to do His work. Scripture tells us God works that way, to confound the wise. What He really wants is an obedient and open heart — to hear Him and then to do what He says. Obedience is the linking element.

The link between spiritual and natural events was a primary focus of each feast. And it is the most important fact to remember in relation to barley. There is every reason to expect the spiritual and natural to work together when we walk in obedience to God's design for our sustenance and restoration. He perfects us as we obey Him.

OFFERING THE FIRSTFRUITS

Now that we have had an overview of the feasts of Israel, let us focus on barley itself as the firstfruits of the barley harvest. It is fascinating to imagine how good those bright green shoots of barley must have looked to the ancient Hebrews after a winter of dried and preserved foods and little enough to eat of even "the same old stuff." No wonder their hearts told them of God's power and provision made manifest in this first crop of spring.

It is not at all difficult for me to imagine that these tender young shoots were used as food by the ancient Hebrews. In fact, it is hard to imagine how they could resist this perfect spring tonic!

This was the crop that, in God's perfect will, would renew and restore both His people and their animals after the long winter of nutritionally meager foods. It would strengthen them by cleansing accumulated internal toxins, poisons and metabolic ashes.

This fact is substantiated so well by a research study done in the early 1930's here in the United States by Dr. Schnabel. His study showed that animals who lived in the wild in frigid temperatures would show great improvement in their health in just two or three weeks time after being pastured in fields of young, tender grass.

How providential that we have green barley to do this for us after the "long winter" of nutritionally meager overprocessed and non-nourishing foods!

A FIRSTFRUITS PEOPLE

Another point for meditative consideration: we are, through our union with Christ, a firstfruits people ourselves. It is worth our time, I think, to consider this fact in terms of sowing and reaping.

Both Paul (in Galatians 6:7,8) and James, the

brother of our Lord, (in James 1:14-18) warn us that we will reap what we sow. If we sow a crop of disobedience to God's laws in the realm of nutrition and health, we're not likely to make a very perfect or lively sacrifice, are we? We won't even be in fighting condition when the enemy tries to steal a march on us! The lusts of the body will cause us to reap a harvest of destruction, as Scripture warns us.

If, on the other hand, we are willing to sow good seed to our bodies, eating what is not only physically but spiritually good for us, we will reap a double blessing. Our bodies will be perfected as a suitable temple for the living God, and we will be in excellent condition should attack come from our enemies.

In doing this, we will be like the wise virgins or the good servants in the Master's parables. And, like barley, we will be available and nourishing to those around us.

GOD'S SPECIAL 'BARLEY PEOPLE'

This brought forth another idea: it is easy to see for ourselves that among professing Christians there are several distinct levels of commitment to discipleship. As one pastor said, there are curious disciples, convicted disciples and committed disciples. I can see how these types can be compared to various grains.

For example, let's take rye first and compare it to

being a curious disciple. This type of "inferior wheat," as it is often called, is not the kind that is in great demand. It is easily threshed, but it comes to harvest later than the other grains, for it requires all of the "latter rains" in order to mature.

Then there is wheat — the grain that is called the staff of life. It is always threshed and ground before it can be best used. It can take being whipped, flailed, and tossed about without damage. It is even ground by being bruised, crushed and reduced to powder. The wheat people make up the greater portion of the consumed grain. They represent the convicted disciples who are the real backbone of Christianity.

Now comes the best for last. God has a small group of barley people, I believe, who truly are the committed ones. Exodus 21:5 describes these *bond-slaves* as those who love their master so much that they want to become a *volunteer permanent slave.* They are the ones who only require winnowing — being fanned, as opposed to beaten, by a current of air to separate the chaff from the grain. These barley people just need to be exposed to the wind of the Holy Spirit to have the waste material fall off and be blown away. No heavy bruising, repeated striking or grinding as in the case of the other grains.

The barley people have always shown superior character qualities. They too thrive in cold climates, unfriendly circumstances, without lots of rain, and they resist the conditions of disease and filth in their environment. They want to be pure, holy, righteous — yes, even perfect as is their heavenly Father.

CHOOSING QUALITY

On a more practical level, I think it is important to notice that God designed our bodies so that they would be built up, cell by cell, by what we put into them. Not only that, our cells are designed to keep choosing the very best of what we put into them and eliminate whatever is of poorer quality. Let's take a look at this concept.

CELL SELECTION IN ACTION

In order to fully appreciate our need for barley and the way its design and our human systems are *made for each other*, it is important to understand one of the basic principles of cell biology. It is the principle of **cell selection**. (For a more detailed discussion of this, see Chapter 3 of my book, *GREEN LEAVES OF BARLEY: A Food with Real Power*).

Although its mechanisms are, and are likely to remain, far beyond human comprehension, the principle itself is elegantly simple. **Cell Selection** means that, of all the substances available to it at any given point in time, **each cell in your body has the ability to select the best available nutrients;** and what is more, it makes room for it by **dumping whatever is the worst** for it at that point.

As awesome as it is to contemplate this kind of wisdom built right into your body, it is even more so when we begin to understand implications and work them out in terms of nutrition and health. It builds my faith just looking at these processes! They were clearly designed by an Intelligence so far above ours that our own intelligence, if it is really seeing the truth, will certainly acknowledge His Lordship.

PERFECTION DESIGNED INTO THE STRUCTURE OF BARLEY

Remembering that what is true spiritually must reveal its nature right down to the level of molecular structure, let's take a closer look at the structure of barley. We have learned that God's way of protecting us is to perfect us. In looking at the principle of cell selection, we saw that nutrition according to God's plan protects our health by perfecting our cell structure. How is this accomplished in the case of barley?

• Barley grain has been shown by chemical analysis to contain 67 percent carbohydrate and 12 percent protein; scientists today consider this to be the perfect balance for human nutrition.

• Because of its early maturation and hardiness, barley grass requires no artificial fertilizers, herbicides, or pesticides. Therefore, when we look at green barley as a nutritional supplement, we are looking at the concentrated juice of uncontaminated barley grass.

• Green barley is the perfect solution to our problem with getting enough green leafy vegetables into our daily diet. It is an instant food concentrate available at an affordable price.

• Barley grows in alkaline soil, so the concentrate of its leaves tests out as one of the most alkaline of foods. Therefore, green barley is the perfect provision for counteracting the systemic acid condition plaguing so many Americans today.

• Science is slowly discovering that chlorophyll, the "green" found in green barley, may be the perfect, least disruptive treatment for many types of wounds and ulcerations. It has no unpleasant or harmful sideeffects.

• Green barley is an excellent source of the live enzymes we need for perfect health. The American diet with its predominance of cooked food is increasingly "enzymeless."

• Green barley provides protein in the form of "polypeptides," one of the most easily digestible of all proteins.

• Green barley provides a wide spectrum of vitamins and minerals in a nearly perfect balance.

What bountiful evidence our God provides as He shows us that it is always His will to perfect us, as we become willing to follow His direction. It is clear when we look at these aspects of perfection built into barley that God's nature is written not just into His Word, but into His very creation. Let us praise our mighty, compassionate, and perfect Source of provision!

GIVING OURSELVES TO GOD

Now let's look at what the Bible has to tell us about offering the firstfruits, since we are to be a Firstfruits people in Christ:

• The giving of the firstfruits is in obedience to a direct command from God:

"The first of the firstfruits of thy land thou shalt bring into the house of the Lord thy God" (Exodus 23:19).

•There is an urgency to bringing your firstfruits:

"Thou shalt not delay to offer the first ... unto me"(Exodus 22:29).

• We are not to allow other matters, even eating, to keep us from offering our first and best to God:

"When ye are come into the land...you shall eat neither bread...until the selfsame day that ye have brought an offering unto your God" (Leviticus 23:10-14).

• God expects your offering to be the best you have to give:

"All the best...they shall offer unto the Lord"
(Numbers 18:12).

• We are to give where our gifts will be properly
used to feed the people spiritually — or even physically, if need be:

"[he] brought the man of God bread of the
firstfruits...And he said, 'Give unto the people, that
they may eat" (2 Kings 4:42).

I hope you have been as nourished as I have by
this **"feast"** of exciting and edifying firstfruit truths.
For our final course, let us pursue the link between
the natural and spiritual even more deeply. For that,
as we saw, is the main focus of the feasts.

PRINCIPLES OF SACRIFICE

Let me repeat a concept already mentioned. As
the meaning of the feasts comes into focus through
study and meditation, it becomes clear to me that
**when a feast took place on earth, something took
place in heaven at the same time.** I believe heaven
worked with earth on these occasions. This should
not come as a surprise, for after all, earth is depend-
ent upon God and His plans. Scripture also tells us
that **true worship moves the hand of God on our
behalf.**

It is also clear that **the fulfillment of the feasts is
in Jesus Christ,** the Passover Lamb, who brings
heaven and earth together. It is Jesus who, through

His sacrificial death, resurrection, and ascension into heaven, completed the cycle of atonement. And it is that atoning work that enables us believers to come to the feast, bringing **ourselves** as an offering. This is ultimately the only kind of offering God is interested in. (If you have not yet made this offering of yourself to God through Jesus Christ, He waits...!)

The significance of the Offering of Firstfruits can be summed up in the words of Devin Conner when he said:

> *"So we may say that as the sheaf (Christ) was accepted before Jehovah for Israel (the true believers of all ages, actually) and Israel (the true Church of Jesus Christ) was accepted of Jehovah in that sheaf, so Christ is accepted before God for us and we accepted of God in Christ."* [1]

This statement thrilled my soul when I read it, and I hope it will do the same for you.

ONE SACRIFICE FOR ALL

It is interesting to note that the offering is presented to the Lord in the form of a single sheaf, representing all the offerings. That single sheaf presented to the Lord on the feast day speaks of the person of our Lord Jesus. He IS the sheaf of firstfruits. As Saint Paul wrote to the Corinthians:

> *"But now is Christ risen from the dead, and become the firstfruits of them that slept. For since by*

man came death, by man came also the resurrection of the dead. For as in Adam all die, even so in
Christ shall all be made alive. But every man in his
own order: Christ the firstfruits; afterward they that
are Christ's at his coming. Then cometh the end,
when he shall have delivered up the kingdom of
God, even the Father; when he shall have put down
all rule and all authority and power" (1 Corinthians
15:20-24).

Again and again in the New Testament we see
how the Lord Jesus Christ is the fulfillment of all the
truth symbolized in the firstfruits, and more specifi-
cally as the sheaf that was offered on behalf of all.

• He is the "firstbegotten" of the Father (Hebrews
1:6)

• He is the "firstborn" of Mary (Matthew 1:23-25)

• He is the "firstbegotten of the dead" (Revelation
1:5)

• He is the "firstborn among many brethren"
(Romans 8:29)

• He is the "firstfruits" of the resurrected (1
Corinthians 15:23)

THE PERFECT SACRIFICE

Jesus Christ is indeed the first, the choicest, and
the preeminent "Most Holy One," sanctified by the
Father. He is the sheaf of the firstfruits which the
leaves of barley represent in the Festival of the
Firstfruits.

Let us with gladness receive the gift of God in His Son, walking in all the spiritual benefits it brings. Let us also receive with gratitude the gift of barley, being sure to walk in all the natural benefits it brings. I believe this is what God wanted me to see in my study of barley grass and the firstfruits.

FOOTNOTES

[1] Kevin Conner, *The Feasts of Israel,* Bible Temple, Portland, OR., 1980, p. 72.

CHAPTER THREE

POWER:
Barley & the Mighty Acts of God

When the idea of barley having a spiritual dimension was introduced, you were promised a graphic demonstration of the various traits or qualities built into barley. In this chapter, we will see some of the mighty acts of God that involve barley and demonstrate its power. Let's go straight into the Word and save our discussion for further into the chapter.

THE REDEMPTION OF RUTH

This story begins with Ruth's Israelite father-in-law, Elimelech. There was a famine in his homeland so severe that it affected every aspect of his life. In poor health and depression, he became confused and unable to make wise decisions. We assume this is true, because Elimelech moved his family from "House of Bread" (translation of the Hebrew word

"Bethlehem") to a country established by an evil man named Moab.

Moab had been born of the incestuous relations between Lot and one of his own daughters. He worshiped the false gods, Baal of Peor, and Che-mosh. This latter "god" required child sacrifice as part of worship. Moab had grown into adulthood and had, through greed, extortion, fraud and covet-ousness, established a whole new community called "The Plains of Moab" across the Jordan east of Jericho. [1]

So Elimelech, whose very name meant "My God is King," exchanged his homeland of Judah (Land of Praise) for a land of idolaters. We can only assume, and I do, that he soon adopted the lifestyle of the Moabites. It is the **natural** thing to do. In fact, I have seen it happen to some extent in my own life, as I moved from the Midwest to the deep South to New York City, then to the Far West, and now to Florida.

CONSEQUENCES OF DISOBEDIENCE

One thing is certain — the historical record shows that those who worshiped Baal (an image of a bull cast in metal) ate meat sacrificed to this lifeless god. By this act, they provoked the Lord to anger and a plague broke out among them. Elimelech could easily have fallen prey to this plague, for the Bible tells us that he died after living in the land of Moab for about ten years (Ruth 1:3-5). Can you see a parallel here? Those who choose to live a life of lawlessness put themselves outside the protection of the Most High God and become prey to the plagues which are the natural consequence of disobedience.

Let us pray for the lost who have abandoned the ways of their forefathers and left Judah (land of praise) to live among a community of idolators, taking on their values and practices. They have put themselves in grave danger of such plagues as AIDS, one of the natural consequences of such practices.

Another interesting fact emerges here. The Lord had told the Israelites that they must not intermarry with the Moabites because they would try to turn the hearts of the Hebrews to the worship of their vile gods. We find that both Elimelech's sons had ignored God's admonition, and they, too, had died.

From the Hebrew translation of their names, it looks like both boys had suffered poor health from birth, for Mahlon means "sickly" and Chilion means "wasting." How important it is, when a child is in poor health, to obey God's laws and choose a wholesome environment! In this case, it turned out to be a matter of "life and death" importance.

NAOMI'S WITNESS

Elimelech's wife was a "pleasant" person, for this is what the word Naomi means. After she was widowed, she decided to return to her homeland, Israel, where the true God was worshiped. She had heard how the Lord had blessed His people who had remained in Bethlehem and she wanted to return there to live out her life. Naomi apparently wanted to carry through on making God her King, as Elimelech should have done.

It seems that Naomi's witness was strong, even while living among the idolaters, for one of her Moabite daughters-in-law was determined to go and live with her, leaving her homeland of idol worshipers for the land of the One True God.

Ruth renounced all that she could be expected to hold dear in Moab, and voluntarily decided to go to Judah to begin an entirely new life. The Word makes it so clear that this is the step required of every person who desires a real life with the True God, now and forever. We must forsake our old ways and seek the ways of the Lord with all our hearts.

BECOMING GOD'S VESSEL

Ruth, a name that means "friend" in Hebrew, was about to begin a journey that would change her life completely. In fact, it would change the course of history and prepare the way for the entrance of God Himself into human life and flesh.

What did she do that made her fit to become the vessel of God's will? A few very basic and rather difficult things that all of us must face, in order to become truly God's own.

First, she was true to herself. Remember, her nature was expressed as "friend" in the very meaning of the name Ruth. She was willing to take the risks and lay aside her selfish interests on behalf of her friendship with Naomi. In doing so, she became the very essence of the meaning of "friend," remembered and revered down through the ages.

How difficult it is, this process of becoming thoroughly honest with one's self. God can only accept our lives after we have had the courage to face who we are without Him. If Ruth had not had the courage to face who she would be without Naomi and Naomi's God, she would not have seen what she had to do in time. This kind of radical self-honesty and integrity is a difficult road to follow, but it leads to real growth.

Secular psychology has a point in urging the individual to "be yourself" — authentic — to claim your own problems and talents and selfhood. But that is only the first step. It can never lead to an experience of validation in the deepest sense, unless and until that person, having made the tough decision to be "who I really am" finds the only truly meaningful reason for claiming selfhood: giving that true self to the True God.

THE PATH OF OBEDIENCE

Once Ruth had made that crucial decision to be — to give her life in service to Naomi and Naomi's

God — she takes the next step. She chooses the path of obedience, and puts herself in line with God's design for her life.

In doing this, she becomes the earthly vessel of grace through whom God's plan for sending us Jesus Christ can be put into motion. Let us see how this comes about and how God uses barley to put Ruth in the right position and keep her lined up with grace.

If you don't have your Bible out yet, this would be a good time to go and get it. We have just reached the end of chapter one of the book of Ruth. This is where the story really gets exciting. Take a break for a few minutes and read all four chapters, and then come back. We'll just wait for you right here.

Well, where do we find Ruth at the beginning of the second chapter? In a barley field! She has just put herself in the place which will yield all the benefits that God has in mind for her. And isn't this just what happens to the believer who takes up a position in Christ?

COMMITMENT AND COURAGE

Remember now that barley, the firstfruit, is a type of Christ, our Firstfruit. I believe you will also find that when you make up your mind to follow God's will for you in bearing much fruit, you will find that barley will put you "in position" to reap His blessings and all the benefits of physical health, with strength to serve. Let us follow her path of obedience and see how it leads to blessing.

Why was she in that barley field in the first place? She was working hard to provide for Naomi, following through on her commitment. This can't have been easy for Ruth, newly widowed, tired from her journey, a stranger in a strange land. But her commitment gave her the courage to serve, in obedience to the ways and customs of her adopted people.

OBEDIENCE AND PROVISION

God had instructed His people to provide for the widows and destitute by leaving the gleanings of the harvest for those who were in need. So the first thing Ruth finds in following the path of obedience is provision. In this she takes her place beside Abraham and all the faithful who have proved Jehovah Jireh the True God by experiencing His provision.

She also expresses hope — an indispensable partner to obedience and commitment. Without it, the obedient quickly fall prey to the enemy's temptation to discouragement and disobedience. So we find an obedient Ruth in a field of barley, serving Naomi in the way God has provided, and expressing the hope that she will find favor. God finds her "positionally righteous" just as He finds the believer who takes up that lawful position in Christ, with the hope of finding favor. And it comes as no surprise to the believer that she finds it.

THE FRUITS OF OBEDIENCE

The one who is ultimately responsible for her welfare, her *Kinsman Protector*, wastes no time in showing up on the scene. When he finds out about her commitment and her obedience, he calls her to him, and begins giving her instructions. Just so does the Lord God, our Protector, as we begin to walk in conviction and obedience, positioning ourselves in the "field" of His Firstfruit, Christ Jesus.

Thus begins a romance that will live forever, both as the story of a woman committed to the God of truth and love; and in the fruit of that romance, our Lord Jesus Christ. For Ruth does not question or protest any of the detailed instructions she receives from her guide, Naomi, or her protector, Boaz, who becomes her husband. The result of Ruth's obedience is God's provision and protection.

God brings about the fulfillment of her commitment to Naomi in bringing a son into the world to provide for this faithful widow's old age. And at the same time, God begins moving in power and majesty to fulfill His promise to all the faithful, for Ruth's son Obed is the father of Jesse, whose son David becomes that king from whose line will come the Messiah.

Let us, like Ruth, find our fulfillment in obedience to God, putting ourselves in the right position to receive God's mighty power into our lives!

MORE MIGHTY ACTS IN OTHER FIELDS

Just so the believer doesn't miss the point of taking up the proper position to receive God's blessings, there are two more stories about mighty acts of God that take place in the middle of a field of barley. The first takes place just three generations later when Ruth's great grandson, David, faces the Philistine army arrayed for battle at Pas Dammim. David and one of his "men of might," Eleazar, had the job of rallying the Israelite army. We read in 1 Chronicles 11:13,14 (NIV),

> *"At a place where there was a field full of barley, the troops fled from the Philistines. But they took their stand in the middle of the field. They defended it and struck the Philistines down, and the Lord brought about a great victory."*

Here is the message as I see it, in the plainest of terms: if you want to be an overcomer in the Lord, take up your position in the right place. Spiritually speaking, that would always be in Jesus, our Firstfruit. Physically, we would be taking a firm stand in favor of God's plan for health through food from the earth. We will soon see that barley is clearly shown to be in important food for the overcomer.

RESPONDING TO THE GOOD NEWS

One more field — this one is a pasture, so there are probably a number of different members of the grass family here, including barley.

Remember our naturalist pointing out that grasses keep the soil from eroding away ... that sounds like the verse in Colossians, "in him all things hold together" (Col. 1:17 NIV).

At any rate, we are dealing with *grass roots* support in this episode. It is the angels' announcement of the birth of Jesus, (in the second chapter of Luke) 17 generations after Ruth; and it takes place in the pasture right next to the barley field where Boaz and Ruth played their part in the coming of the King.[2]

This particular mighty act speaks to us of readiness to hear Good News and act upon it. Let us be ready to do this both in the spiritual realm and in the nutritional one as well. After all, the shepherds that were witnesses to the angelic choirs sought out Jesus "with haste," and having found Him, went out and spread the news to everyone they met. We could easily benefit from walking in those footsteps.

BARLEY BREAD AND THE OVERCOMER

I believe the Lord has more to tell us about barley, this time in the symbol of barley bread. In the Old Testament Book of Judges, we find the story of Gideon.

> *"The Midianites, the Amalekites and all the other eastern peoples had settled in the valley, thick as locusts. Their camels could no more be counted that the sand on the seashore.*
>
> *Gideon arrived just as a man was telling a friend his dream. 'I had a dream,' he was saying. 'A round loaf of barley bread came tumbling into the Midianite camp. It struck the tent with such force that the tent overturned and collapsed.'*
>
> *His friend responded, 'This can be nothing other than the sword of Gideon son of Joash, the Israelite. God has given the Midianites and the whole camp into his hands' "* (Judges 7:12-14 NIV).

Here God uses "a loaf of barley" as a symbol for Gideon, who fulfills this dream/prophecy by wiping out the Midianite hordes with 300 faith-filled warriors. Gideon is perhaps best-known for "laying down a fleece" to make sure he had heard from the Lord. Once he received confirmation, he was instructed by the Lord to select only the fearless from his army of 22,000.

The first cut was from 22,000 down to 3,000, but the Lord was not satisfied yet — He had in mind a victory that was so miraculous that Israel could not possibly think it came from their might of arms, but only through Jehovah God's mighty power to save!

It was then that God showed Gideon how to further select only the 300 men that were totally prepared, psychologically and spirtually, for battle.

Once this had been accomplished, Gideon was still somewhat apprehensive, so the Lord sent him down to the enemy camp to hear the dream/prophecy we just read.

Having heard this, he worships God, then returns to his 300 men and tells them that the Lord has surely given their enemy into their hands. Gideon and his little band go forth to get the victory God has planned.

This image of Gideon symbolized as a loaf of barley really intrigued me. Looking back over the entire story in Judges, chapters 6-9, with that symbolism in mind reveals many hidden truths about barley. First, open your Bible and read with me through these chapters; then, let me tell you how the Lord made sure I gave it my attention.

BARLEY AS 'MIGHTY WARRIOR'

In the spring of 1987 I went to California to make a speech. While I was there, my hostess shared with me some special insights into two of the Scriptures on barley.

The first was the one in 1 Chronicles 11:13 that we read a little earlier in the chapter. This is where David and Eleazar get the victory in a field of barley at Pas Dammim. She was shown that we, like the mighty men of ancient days, will get the victory for the Lord with the help of barley. Let me add my enthusiastic "amen" to that!

The second was the Scripture quoted just above, where Gideon overhears the Midianite's dream of Israel's victory. The fascinating aspect of this story (Judges 7:12-14) is that God uses barley as a symbol for a mighty warrior, Gideon.

According to the insight my hostess felt God had given her, the "enormous enemy" (Midianites) over-running God's children (the Israelites) today is "physical infirmities," and God's answer to our weakness and illness and obesity and chronic complaints will be found in good nutrition and barley! What an exciting confirmation of the insights I felt God had been granting me.

SPOTLIGHT ON GIDEON

Several weeks later I heard more from my new friend, who had become very excited over the Word God has for us in the story of Gideon and the barley loaf. She wrote to me at length about Judges 6, 7 and 8. I would like to share some of her insights with you. She writes,

> *"I must admit I have never been in such awe of the Word of God as in doing this study and finding the minute details in these three chapters which show the enemies (represented by Midian and the hordes from the East) to be, in fact, hunger, overeating, and the sicknesses and diseases in consequence. In these Scriptures, God shows us that barley can come into your body (tent) and deliver you from these enemies. This*

*truth from Judges 7:13 is confirmed throughout the
story of Gideon in Judges 6 through 8."*

In this study, the point to notice is that Gideon is
represented by barley bread. When we look at this
symbolism in depth, we can see barley is portrayed
here as mighty, like Gideon whose name means
"great warrior." Thus, I believe barley is being shown
here as nutritionally mighty and a great warrior
against the sickness and diseases which attack the
body.

'TOO MUCH' AND 'TOO MANY'

In *Unger's Bible Dictionary*, we find that the
Midianites and their cohorts were innumerable
hordes of camel-riding nomads. To quote from
Unger's, they *"oppressed Israel, not by a strong
military despotism, backed by chariots of iron, but
by coming up when the harvest was ripe like locusts
or grasshoppers, and destroying the increase of the
earth."*

We also read in Unger's, *"they were formidable
from their vast numbers and hunger." They were
destroying Israel, not by force of arms, but by tram-
pling the harvest in their nomadic wanderings, and
by stealing and devouring the Israelite's foodstores."*

So Midianites represent hunger, and from our
typology we see barley will fight to overcome hunger, curbing our appetites by satisfying the cravings

of our cells for good nutrition. Midianites also represent *too many, too much,* thus, *overeating.*

(I have read and heard testimonies from many people telling how their appetites have been altered by taking green leaves of barley. Their long-time tendency to overeat was changed naturally and as a result they report a weight loss — many times a very significant one).

NUTRITIONAL STARVATION

In addition, we see that Midian also represents food destroyed, thus causing starvation for Israel. In the same way, we starve when we do not eat God's food. When we let the "hordes of Midian" get the upper hand we glut out on the wrong food, (food that **doesn't belong to us**), then we starve nutritionally.

If ever there was a perfect example of this, it is here and now in what is happening in America. We have done to God's food supply what we have done to God's Word: watered it down until we no longer get a strong enough dose for our healing and strengthening.

The Bible makes it very clear that one of the most important foods for God's people is barley. So the blessing of barley is twofold: it helps fight hunger, at the same time building us up nutritionally so that our bodies are not in a state of malnutrition — a kind of "semi-starvation."

JEHOVAH-SHALOM

It is here that God chooses to reveal Himself as
Jehovah-Shalom, God of Peace. In Judges 6, the
23rd verse, God says to Gideon, *"Peace be unto
thee; fear not: thou shalt not die."* While Midian
means "strife," God comes with His "shalom," peace.

If you have a fear of obesity and are constantly
plagued with hunger, it is at this point God can
reveal Himself to you as Jehovah-Shalom, just as He
revealed Himself to Gideon in this way when he was
suffering fear of the Midianites. Barley will bring
peace to your body, according to God's Word, by
satisfying the nutritional cravings of your cells.

MIGHTY DELIVERANCE

In Judges 8:28 (NIV), the story of Gideon ends,
*"Thus Midian was subdued before the Israelites and
did not raise its head again. During Gideon's life-
time, the land enjoyed peace forty years."* I believe
you will see that once we make barley our "daily
bread," overeating and hunger will never again raise
their heads to tempt and destroy us. Praise the Lord!

Unger's says, *"...certainly Midian was never again
mentioned as a source of terror."* Neither will overeating and hunger be, when we have the peace of
God's deliverance food, barley. In Judges 6:14b
(NIV), God says to Gideon (barley), *"Go in the
strength you have and save Israel (God's people) out*

of Midian's hand *(overeating). Am I not sending you?"* (Words in parentheses added). Let us, like Israel of old, receive that mighty deliverance.

REDEMPTIVE POWER

There is another aspect of the power in barley that was brought to my attention through the inspired notes of a pastor whose name is unknown. In the 27th chapter of Leviticus, the laws and rules for the redemption of various persons and things are laid out.

In verse 16, we read that if a man dedicated to the Lord part of his family farm, its value was to be set according to the amount of barley seed it produced. It was worth 50 shekels of silver for every homer of barley seed.

No other possible crop on the field is mentioned. Could it be, then, that no other grain had the redemptive power of barley in the mind and plan of God? We only know that the redemption price for a field was determined according to the barley it produced.

I think it is highly interesting to note that the price per measure of barley is exactly the same as the price set for the redemption of a full-grown man in his prime (see Leviticus 27:3). The redemption price of a man and the unit of redemption for a field being dedicated to the Lord are the same.

Could we conclude from this that God made barley to redeem the life and health of man by making barley the highest possible crop? Again, I say I believe so. I believe that green barley leaves have the ability to redeem us from poor health to restore us from sickness to wholeness. Further insight into this redemptive power is shared in Chapter Five.

THE MIRACLES OF THE BARLEY LOAVES

Before we leave the study of power in barley, we must visit the shores of the Sea of Galilee and take into our spirits a deeper meaning of the miracle of the loaves and fishes.

But let us look first at a miracle in the Old Testament that foreshadows the feeding of the 5,000. Turn with me to the second book of Kings where we join Elisha. There was a famine in the land and beginning in 2 Kings 4:42 we read:

"And there came a man came from Baal-shalisha, and brought the man of God bread of the firstfruits, twenty loaves of barley, and full ears of corn in the husk thereof. And he said, Give unto the people that they may eat. And his servitor said, What, should I set this before a hundred men? He said again, Give the people that they may eat: for thus saith the Lord, They shall eat, and shall leave thereof. So he set it before them, and they did eat, and left thereof, according to the word of the Lord."

Here we have barley as the firstfruits, shadowing forth the power of Christ, the true Firstfruit, to accomplish all that God has for Him, and more, a super-abundance.

This is also a type of the miracle of loaves and fishes beside the Sea of Galilee (John 6:9). Here Jesus provides, in a show of incredible power and might, for the feeding of 5,000 men with their families from five barley loaves and two fish.

Why barley loaves? Barley is specified in both these mighty acts, where in many places we have simply "loaves" or "bread." I believe there is a special spiritual significance to God's specifying barley loaves here.

First of all, barley is used as a symbol and confirmation that Jesus is His Chosen One, His Firstfruit, the perfect sacrifice. But I believe He is also saying to us, Christ's followers, that we are to feed our bodies with barley, as Jesus fed His followers beside the Sea of Galilee that day. There is a special power to putting ourselves in line with God's design.

GOD'S MIGHTY POWER MANIFEST IN BARLEY

There is a way of choosing food in accordance with wise principles: principles designed into God's creation (nutritional science is the branch of knowledge which concerns itself with the discovery of these) and principles revealed to us in His Word.

To my mind, one conclusion seems evident from the stories in this chapter. As we feed on the barley that God has provided and portrayed in His Word as mighty, we are enabled to walk in victory, receiving health and healing through His mighty power manifested in barley.

FOOTNOTES

[1] Charles Pfeiffer and Everett Harrison, Editors, *The Wycliffe Bible Commentary,* The Moody Bible Institute, Chicago, IL, 1962, p. 268.

[2] Henry H. Halley, *Halley's Bible Handbook,* 24th Edition, Zondervan Publishing House, Grand Rapids, MI, 1965, p. 176.

CHAPTER FOUR

PROTECTION:
Barley as a Spiritual Weapon

In the story of Elisha and the brotherhood of prophets in 2 Kings 4, God uses barley to protect His people from poisoning and starvation. How many of us have come to the conclusion that the "pop culture" way of eating in America today has a lot in common with both poisoning and starvation?

Further on in this chapter we will take a look at what biomedical research has to say about some of the protective factors in barley leaves. It seems science, after the work of several centuries, may be catching on to the purposes of the One who created it all to work perfectly together in the first place!

PROTECTION FROM POISONING

First, travel back in time with me to the day of Elisha the prophet. At the time of our story, there was a famine in the land. The prophet and his servant had traveled to Gilgal to meet with a "brotherhood of prophets," numbering about 100 men. The season was early spring, because we are told of a man bringing fresh barley in the ear.

Elisha has Gehazi, his servant, put a large pot on the fire and make some soup for the brotherhood. One of the brothers, thinking to be helpful, went into the fields to gather herbs for the pot.

While he was out gathering, he came across a *"wild vine off which he gathered enough gourds to fill his lap. On his return, he cut them up into the pot of soup; they did not know what they were"* (2 Kings 4:39, JB).

Now, right there, those of you who are cautious and conservative by nature will begin saying to yourselves, "Why would anyone be so foolish as to eat something they had never seen before?" But most of us are doing just that, every day. There are so many additives and preservatives we glibly swallow without knowing anything about them; and some of them really are poison.

Remember, they were in mid-famine, and Satan can be very deceitful. A whole flock of hungry prophets are assembled here. Somehow it just doesn't seem likely he would pass up a chance like this.

"They then poured the soup out for the men to eat, but they had no sooner tasted the soup than

*they cried, 'Man of God, there is death in the pot!'
And they could not eat it" (2 Kings 4:40 JB).*

BARLEY VS. THE WORKS OF THE ENEMY

In the light of modern scientific findings, it is fascinating what the prophet Elisha does next. When Old Testament prophets act on God's behalf, they nearly always do so with some symbol of power and authority, like a staff held forth or arms upraised.

In this case, the symbol of power used is barley meal. And the power is used to counteract the work of the enemy, who has taken this opportunity to attack God's prophets through the stress of starvation and the mechanism of their bodily hunger.

When you read 2 Kings 4:41, you will not see the word "barley" in the verse. Nevertheless, I am quite comfortable with the assumption that the "meal" Elisha asks for in the verse is barley meal, and I will show you why.

Look at the next verse, 2 Kings 4:42. A man has come from another area bringing Elisha *"bread from the firstfruits, twenty barley loaves and fresh grain in the ear."*

This tells us it was at barley harvest time, or shortly thereafter. Since storage techniques of that time were not like ours (whether that is a blessing or otherwise I leave up to you), I think it is a reasonable assumption the meal Elisha uses is barley meal.

Here is another reason I think it was barley: look at the results. Elisha threw the meal into the pot and told them to eat it. *"And there was nothing harmful in the pot."* That's how verse 41 ends.

FAITH, BARLEY & SPIRITUAL WARFARE

This has traditionally been regarded as one of the miracles of Elisha, and I certainly regard it as a mighty act of God done through the faith of one of His greatest prophets.

However, I find it very interesting that modern science actually confirms and details the power hidden inside barley to counteract poisons. Not that modern science is the least bit willing to understand such things as poisons as weapons of the enemy. But I certainly believe in a **spiritual warfare** that is carried on through **poisons** on the one hand, and **protective elements** in raw natural foods like barley on the other.

Let's look at the marvelous chemicals called enzymes God has provided to perfect and protect us.

PROVISION OF ENZYMES IN GOD'S HEALTH PLAN

Enzymes are the catalysts that perform and serve as expediters for the body's myriad chemical reactions without which we cannot survive. Enzymes are required at every step of the metabolic process: to

decompose and digest the food we eat, to disperse
the vitamins and minerals into the bloodstream, and
to enable the cells to absorb them.

Even the gas exchange inside your lungs that fur-
nishes your body with life-giving oxygen is only possible because of enzymes. All our motor activities
and even the process of thinking require enzymes.

There is no function of the human body that does
not require enzymes, that does not suffer if their
supply is insufficient, that will not cease without
them. That's the way our Creator designed the system to work — and that is why the provision of God
for our protection and restoration is so clear to me in
the chemical structure of green barley leaves.

According to Dr. Hagiwara, their juice contains
several hundred enzymes corresponding to those
found in human body cells. It is this multitude of enzymes, left **intact and fully alive** by the methods
used in making Barley Green, that makes it a powerful weapon for our defense. The effectiveness of any
food depends upon the way it is processed — and
food which is not subjected to heat above 122° F will
have the greatest provision of nutrients for the body.

PROTECTION FROM POISON THROUGH ENZYMES

One of the most important functions of **enzymes**
is to **neutralize poisons** in the body. Now you can

begin to see why I responded to Elisha's way of
dealing with that poisoned soup with more than
average interest. I believe God was giving us some
information about the specific powers in barley.
And He was doing it thousands of years before
science would catch up with the reality of His
chemical engineering.

There's a whole family of enzymes whose sole
purpose in life is to "resolve" indigestible and even
toxic substances. They do this by turning the harmful
chemical into something harmless: either into something the body can use or into something it can easily
get rid of. Either way, you can see that enzymes are
an awesome provision of God for our protection.

Another family of enzymes provides protection
by tackling destructive "free radicals" and rendering
them harmless.

"I would not have you ignorant, brethren" ... so
let me give you some specifics on one of the more
important enzymes in this family. A powerful provision for our protection from the pollutants we absorb
from air, water and food goes by the impressive
name of superoxide dismutase, or SOD.

SOD AGAINST THE 'FREE RADICAL'

"Free radicals" are highly active and unstable
chemicals constantly produced as by-products of
cellular metabolism in the course of normal diges-

tion and respiration. Stress, poison (like food additives), and pollution can increase the rate at which these are produced, but they are always being produced at some level in the healthiest system. Many of the supposedly "harmless" additives cause considerable stress to the metabolism and add to the free radical problem.

Organ or tissue damage occurs when the production of free radicals exceeds that of the scavenger enzymes. SOD and its cousins roam the system like patrolling firefighters, "putting out" free radicals which would otherwise "burn" or damage unprotected molecules, cells, and tissues.

One of these free radicals is called the "superoxide anion." This radical has been shown to have a very strong oxidizing power capable of exerting a variety of harmful effects: causing cancer and inflammatory disease, even decomposing cells. SOD catalyzes a dismutation reaction that converts it into hydrogen peroxide.

THE LORD JEHOVAH AS BIOCHEMIST

I believe it is no coincidence that God made barley the first crop of spring, knowing that our forebearers would spend the winter indoors around a fire with its attendant smoke and fumes. Science has recently discovered that smoke and fumes of many kinds can cause gene breakage and cell damage by producing a bumper crop of free radicals as the overloaded system tries to deal with these harmful chemicals.

In our time, it is harder and harder to get away from the fire and fumes. Instead of being confined to the winter and the indoors, pollution hazards have become widespread and year-round. Yet, God has provided a way for us to get our barley all year, not just at the spring harvest. And researchers have found that the potent enzymes in green barley actually **increase gene repair activity** at the cellular level. Now, that's protection!

CELLULAR LEVEL SPIRITUAL WARFARE

I once heard of a Bible teacher who called demons "malignant little wads of decisional energy looking for a place to land." When you start looking at the cast of characters at the cellular level, it is easy to see any number of critters that fit that description — poisons, free radicals, cancers, and viruses would all be examples. The enzymes in green barley provide a formidable array of protective chemicals which God intends us to use against these attacks.

PROTECTION AGAINST STARVATION

Another form of divine protection is demonstrated in the second part of this story of Elisha at Gilgal (2 Kings 4:42-44). We have seen these verses before, when we were looking at the mighty acts of God in the chapter on the spiritual power of barley. Now let's look at them from the viewpoint of protection — in this case, protection against starvation.

> *"A man came ... bringing the man of God bread from the firstfruits, twenty barley loaves and fresh grain in the ear. 'Give it to the people to eat,' Elisha said. But his servant replied, 'How can I serve this to a hundred men?' 'Give it to the people to eat,' he insisted, for Yahweh says this, 'They will eat and have some left over.' He served them; they ate and had some left over, as Yahweh had said" (JB).*

As I pointed out in earlier chapters, the nutrient profile of barley is just about perfect. Nearly everything the human system needs is present in ideal proportions. Since barley was very possibly the first cereal grain known to man, it should come as no surprise that God built it so nutritionally perfect.

In the days of Elisha, God's protection was provided in case of actual food shortages like the famine in this story. He designed barley to grow even under adverse conditions — including drought. And He designed it to keep the human system in a healthy balance even if only small amounts were available.

In our day, we have an entirely new kind of starvation staring us in the face: nutritional starvation, which scientists call "malnutrition syndrome."

It is entirely possible to spend $100 at the supermarket and get about $5 worth of quality nutrition.

By the time your metabolism gets through dealing with the hazardous chemicals in the processed food, you may actually be in a deficit situation: the stress of handling the "non-food food" has actually outweighed the metabolic benefits received from the meal itself.

That is one reason I feel so strongly about green barley. In this nutritious concentrate, God has provided the elements needed to bring balance to our nutrition and to protect us from the destructive aspects of modern processed food.

PROTECTION, PERFECTION & HEALTH

Both stories tell us of the protection of God's people. Barley is used to provide this protection, but just as with any other weapon, success depends greatly on knowing how to use it and on our reliance on God. It would be hard to miss that lesson even if the only Bible story we knew was "David and Goliath!"

Elisha could not have done those works if it hadn't been for his faith in God. In the same way, we must understand the natural/spiritual linkage that makes barley so potent. **AND** we must understand God's way of bringing about health and healing.

In Chapter One, we talked about God's health plan. It was there that the concept of protection through perfection first was explained. God's way of protecting us from the dangers of poison, starvation, stress, and disease is to make our bodies so that they are constantly working towards perfection. The mechanism of cell selection is a primary example.

When we looked into the concept of cell selection, we found that there is a God-given talent possessed by every one of our cells to choose the highest possible quality nutrients from whatever is available to it at any given time. If we follow the implications of this carefully, we will see that the human system is continually being protected and perfected through what we assimilate from what we eat.

A further implication bears more thought than we are used to giving it, perhaps. It is perfectly obvious that benefiting from **God's health plan** depends on knowing its principles and eating according to **God's food plan**, (natural foods processed as little as possible). But perhaps there are things we put into our bodies that hinder the working out of God's health plan.

PROTECTION, PREVENTION, MEDICINE

It should be abundantly clear by now that we must be aware of what we are putting into our bodies, since God made them to produce health by assimilating the health-giving substances in fresh natural food. Cell selection and resolution of harmful substances by enzymes found in raw food are just two reasons we need to be very diligent in going along with God's plan.

But more and more often in these modern times, health and healing are thought of as having to do with doctors and medicine. In our search for health, we sometimes put our confidence in substances and procedures that may not help; in fact, some drugs and treatments may actually block the processes God designed to keep us healthy.

For instance, antibiotics are certainly a blessing when used in emergencies and according to strict diagnostic guidelines. But caution must be used by both doctors and patients to see they are not over-used, for many either block or work against the natural processes of recovery and renewal of health from within. The same could be said of steroids, radiation treatment, even certain kinds of surgery and diagnostic procedures.

This is especially true with regard to our major national health problems, sometimes known as the Big Four: cardiovascular disease, cancer, arthritis, and diabetes. Every one of these is a degenerative disease in some sense, meaning that the onset follows a period of degenerating health and proceeds on a relentless course of degeneration once it has been diagnosed.

While medical science continues to make progress in high-tech methods of diagnosis and treatment, a moment's reflection will bring us to the startling conclusion that medicine has no cure for any of these. The reason is because these degenerative diseases have only one cure: **PREVENTION!** Medical science seems strangely slow to pursue this approach, with the exception of a very few prevention-oriented practitioners.

Let's take a look at what the Bible has to say about health and doctors in the apocryphal book of Ecclesiasticus, containing some of the wisdom of the early Christian church fathers.

THE ROLE OF MEDICINE AND THE DOCTOR IN GOD'S PLAN

It is interesting to note that in Ecclesiasticus 38:1-15 (JB) there is a clear directive for what steps the ill should take to recover their health. While we are told that healing itself comes from the Most High, like a gift from a king, we are to honor the doctor in return for his services.

It is especially significant, I believe, to read in verse 4 of this chapter that God brought medicines into existence *"from the earth"* — not from purified chemicals! That phrase "from the earth" is in perfect harmony with what Scripture says is the source of man's creation and sustenance in Genesis 1; little wonder, then, that these natural products work.

"The sensible man will not despise them" for

"He uses them to heal and to relieve pain" (Ecclesiasticus 38:4,7).

Another concept found in these verses tells us we should not be depressed when we are ill. Rather, we should "pray to the Lord and He will heal." This is similar to the principle in Isaiah 53:5 where we sing "He was wounded for our transgressions, He was bruised for our iniquities, Surely He bore our sorrows, And by His stripes we are healed." In my experience, the appeal to God for healing is a crucial first priority.

In addition, we are given a specific plan to follow: we are to renounce our faults, keep our hands unsoiled, and make an offering to the Lord. Following these instructions in spiritual disciplines, we are told, *"Then let the doctor take over — the Lord created him too — and do not let him leave you, for you need him" (Ecclesiasticus 38:12).*

Why is it that we need him? Verses 13 and 14 give the answer which, to me, makes such practical sense.

"Sometimes success is in their (the doctors') hands, since they in turn will beseech the Lord to grant them the grace to relieve and to heal, that life may be saved."

How wonderful it would be to have a nation full of God-fearing doctors who pray for their patients! Unfortunately, this is often not the *situation.*

WHY NOT TRUST GOD?

In fact, doctors relate that they have been discouraged from having faith in God in medical school. They are taught to be self-reliant and independent of even the need for divine assistance. Dr. William Standish Reed of the Christian Medical Foundation International Inc., warns that medicine seems to have become a new "religion" in America today.

The incredible fact to me is that many Americans don't even want a doctor who is a praying person. As I write this, I have learned of three cases where doctors were actually taken to court for praying for their patients. They are being sued for the malpractice of medicine!

How truly the Scriptures say, "Man's ways are seldom God's ways." Our response when we become ill these days is, in the vast majority of cases, to immediately seek medical attention. There is hardly a thought given to asking God for help.

Even less do we consider the specific steps laid out so plainly in Ecclesiasticus 38 — cleansing ourselves of wrong-doing and wrong-thinking, and paying our debts to God.

• Have we failed to care for ourselves?
• Have we harbored hatred, jealousy, anxiety?
• Have we fallen away from a commitment we made to God to be good stewards of our health and present our bodies to Him as living sacrifices?

RESEARCH FINDS PRAYER A VALUABLE ADJUNCT TO HOSPITAL TREATMENT

Few of us are willing to make the effort to find a doctor who will pray for us, as Ecclesiasticus suggests. But would having a praying doctor really make a difference in the outcome of the case? Let me share the results of a 1987 research study on that subject. Research at San Francisco General Hospital revealed victims — of heart attack, heart failure, and other cardiac problems — remembered in prayers fared better than those who were not.

Cardiologist Randy Byrd, formerly a University of California professor, said 192 patients in the group prayed for had significantly fewer complications than 201 in the "non-prayer" group. And fewer members of the prayed-for group died.

The researcher said he conducted the study as "a scientific evaluation of what God is doing. After much prayer, the idea of what to do came to me."

During the 10-month study, a computer assigned patients in a coronary intensive care unit either to a group that was the focus of prayers by home prayer groups or to a group that was unremembered in prayer. Patients, doctors, and nurses did not know which group patients were in.

First names, diagnoses, and prognoses of patients were given to prayer groups scattered around the country. Members of the prayer groups individually petitioned God daily for the recovery of the patients throughout their hospital stays.

The researcher said the results were dramatic. He found that none of the prayed-for had to be placed on breathing devices, while 12 of those not prayed for needed respirators.

The prayed-for group was five times less likely than the 'unremembered' to develop a lung condition that leads to heart failure.

Fewer patients who were prayed for died, but the trend was not statistically significant, noted Byrd, whose findings have been published in the proceedings of the American Heart Association.

Dr. William Nolen, author of a book debunking faith healing, said he was impressed with Byrd's study. *"It sounds as if this study will stand up to scrutiny,"* said the Litchfield, Minnesota, surgeon. Nolen, a Catholic, said he doesn't pray for his patients, but that, based on this study, maybe he should. [1]

If science is able to prove the efficacy of prayer for healing in a research setting, we who are Christians should be all the more ready to do things "God's way" in regard to physical health as well as spiritual.

Let us strengthen our Christian witness by strengthening our physical well-being, not only through prayer, but also by following Elisha's example: faith — and barley!

FOOTNOTES

[1] *Chicago Sun Times,* Science section, January, 1986.

Chapter 5

REDEMPTION:
The Power in the Blood

We have come nearly full circle in our study of the spiritual roots of barley. I have two stories for you in this chapter, a sort of "alpha and omega" of the principle of redemption, the provision of power for our protection and perfection.

REDEMPTION AND OBEDIENCE IN THE DELIVERANCE OF ISRAEL

The very first reference to barley in the Bible is found in Exodus 9:31 where it says, *"The flax and the barley was smitten: for the barley was in the ear, and the flax was bolled."* The significance of this passage is not immediately apparent, however, without some background provided in terms of what is going on at this point in history.

Moses and his brother, Aaron, had been given an

assignment by God. Their mission was to go to Egypt and rescue the Israelites who were enslaved to Pharoah. When accomplished, this would fulfill God's promise to Abraham, Isaac, and Jacob, that their descendants would occupy the Promised Land.

The Bible provides the story of their mission in fascinating details, but for our present study, let us focus on the plagues God inflicted upon Egypt in consequence of Pharoah's hard heart. It would take fully ten plagues before Pharoah would let God's people go. (Even then, he changed his mind after he had let them leave, but that's another story … .)

The first nine plagues were all "natural wonders" — intensified experiences of distresses with which they were already familiar. They were marked as miraculous because of their unusually quick appearance and disappearance. But they left a deep impression on the Egyptians because each plague was directed against some aspect of nature worshiped by the Egyptians — frogs, lice, cattle, locusts, and so forth.

THE BLOOD OF A LAMB

The tenth and last plague was different from the other nine. God actually visited the families and fulfilled the promise He had given in warning of what He would do if Pharaoh failed to repent. All firstborn sons were to die, from the firstborn son of

Pharaoh right down to the firstborn son of the slave girl. But the firstborn sons of the Israelites who followed God's instructions for salvation, staining their doorposts and lintels with the blood of a lamb, were not to be slain. They were "passed over," thus showing in a supernatural way the distinction God had made between the Egyptians and the obedient Israelites.

BARLEY AND THE SEVENTH PLAGUE

Barley enters this picture at the time of the seventh plague — thunder, lightning, and hail. The hail fell on men and animals and on everything growing in the fields of Egypt (Exodus 9:22-26). It was in this plague that the flax and the barley were destroyed.

The six words, *"the flax and barley were destroyed" (Exodus 9:31 NIV),* seem so insignificant; like a short postscript to a long letter. But let me explain why I believe these words are full of power and principle.

As you have seen in other segments of this book, barley is pictured in some Scriptures as a "mighty warrior." Barley will redeem the body from hunger, sickness and stress. In fact, as we see in Leviticus 27:16, barley is the only crop mentioned in the context of redemption. Let me show you how I believe God is illustrating the principle of redemption in this passage.

AN EGYPTIAN'S STORY

Let's make this story personal, getting inside the skin of an Egyptian for a few days. Here is what we would have heard.

"First, our entire water supply turned to blood and we had no water to drink. The rivers, canals, marshes, and reservoirs, even the water stored in our toilet bowls and in containers in the refrigerator turned to blood.

"The fish all died and the whole countryside stank until our heads ached. This lasted long enough to fray our nerves. After all, we could not take baths, wash our dirty clothes or dirty cars, water our house-plants, or do anything routine that required water. This ended on Friday. What a relief!

"The very next week, however, we were hit with another freak experience. Our property was covered from one side to the other with hordes of frogs. They came into our houses, right into our bedrooms and even into our beds. Our children were screaming and we would have too, if we had dared.

"In the morning we turned on the oven to fix breakfast but it was full of frogs, as were our pots and pans, including the kneading bowls (Exodus 8:5-7). Our whole house was literally immersed in a sea of frogs! The swimming pool was invisible from the kitchen window — it looked like a new green carpet had been stretched over the water.

"We were exasperated, harried, exhausted —

ready to give up. Can you imagine what the clean-up was like when they finally died? They were piled into great heaps and made a terrific stench throughout the countryside (Exodus 8:13, 14).

"We were just beginning to recover from the frogs when, lo and behold, millions of lice infested our place — cattle, horses, camels, cats, dogs, chickens — even the wild beasts and birds had them. Our whole nation was filled with lice, and we didn't even have any protective ointment to use on the children's heads. It was devastating to see our babies and animals suffer — to say nothing of how we personally felt.

"This was followed immediately by swarms of flies like you can hardly imagine — unless you have lived on a farm and have seen some swarms of gnats in August. Bull flies were so large, so strong and so noisy they sounded just like a buzz-saw cutting logs for the fireplace. They were everywhere, literally everywhere.

"All of us were ready for the insane asylum. Anxiety, fear and stress had been coming in mega-doses so continuously that we feared for our sanity, even our lives.

"But that was not all. The very day after the flies had died and been swept up the best we could, all of our cattle began to die. Our horses, donkeys, camels, flocks, and herds — all were deathly ill. So now even our material wealth was being destroyed.

NO OTHER GOD

"All the while our barley had been steadily maturing and was about ready to eat. Barley had always given us a spring-time **pick-up**, renewing our bodies and strengthening us to overcome whatever ailed.

"Our flax, too, was ripening, giving promise of fresh new garments. We were looking forward to the physical and emotional lift provided by the barley and flax crops just maturing."

Right at this point, however, God had a point to make and wanted to make sure none of us would miss it. In forcing Pharaoh to let the children of Israel go by supernatural power, He wanted to prove both to the children of Israel and to the entire Egyptian nation that **THERE IS NO OTHER GOD**. He wanted (and still wants!) everyone on earth to know that there is no redemption except through total reliance on and obedience to Him.

He knows our natural tendency to be self-reliant, self-sufficient and hedonistic. So He removed our last ray of hope in "saving ourselves" when He took out the barley and the flax.

NO OTHER PLAN

We have two important principles of redemption here. Primarily: the first step in redemption is obedience. Second, we find even God's provisions will not avail unless **total reliance on God** comes first.

The Egyptians benefited from the principles built into barley, but God showed them that those who consciously and stubbornly rebel cannot expect to continue reaping those benefits when they refuse the chance to obey.

We must carefully discern a third principle of redemption in order to line ourselves up with God's plan. Just as we see foreshadowed in the story of Moses and the redemption of Israel at Passover, God has a certain method worked out for manifesting the spiritual power of redemption in earthly terms. It is **redemption through the blood.**

When God redeemed Israel out of Egypt, He used the blood of a lamb on the doorposts of Hebrew homes to indicate those obedient to His plan. Those who **applied the blood** according to His directions were the ones He redeemed.

A UNIQUE STORY ABOUT BLOOD

It is well known, through the study of the Scriptures and of the historical record, that in ancient times God required the Jews to make regular sacrifices to atone for their sins. In fact, the blood of animals was required, for *"without shedding of blood is no remission" (Hebrews 9:20, 22).*

From the time of the Passover lamb onward, the priests would offer these blood sacrifices with the words, "This is the blood of the covenant which God has commanded you."

As Christians, we no longer follow the Jewish ceremonial law because God has provided a permanent blood sacrifice for our sins in the blood of Jesus Christ. The true Christian church, regardless of denominational label, teaches the doctrine of salvation through the shed blood of Jesus, the Lamb of God.

This redemption plan was no "emergency measure" on God's part, for the Bible says Jesus is the Lamb slain *"from the foundation of the world" (Revelation 13:8),* for the cleansing of the sins of all generations to follow that event. So God preplanned Jesus to be His perfect sacrificial Lamb. Through our faith in the shedding of His blood at Calvary, we are brought into right relationship with God.

Recently, the Lord opened my mind to see even more deeply into the concept of redemption by the blood. For the first time I saw that God had a more integrated and complete blood cycle at work in the world. This cycle integrated the plants He created on the third day of Creation with man and the other animals He created on the sixth day. The revelation of this concept came to me like this.

CREATED FROM THE EARTH, SUSTAINED BY THE BLOOD

In Genesis 2:7, it is recorded that God created man from the dust of the earth, and breathed into his nostrils the breath of life. Although worldly scientists by the thousands do not accept this statement as fact, it is not a problem for me. I believe it! I have a body which responds so wonderfully to foods grown in the "dust of the earth" that I can believe they were designed to perfect my physical body. They will sustain and renew my body for years and years if I consume the right combination in the right amounts.

I also have a spirit. I know, because Scripture tells me and because His Spirit has revealed it to my spirit, that I am a child of God. I believe, therefore, that God made a physical being and a spiritual being all in the same act of creation. **How does God sustain** this creature that He made in His image and for His glory? The answer is so simple and yet so powerful: **BY BLOOD.**

GREEN SUSTENANCE

Let me explain. In Genesis 1:11 and 1:29, we are told that God made the grass and other herbs and fruit trees for our food. Long before He made us, He made our food supply. (I like that kind of God, don't you?)

The Word says that the grass was made first, and we have seen that there is scientific evidence that this is so. In fact, all the various cereal grains come from grasses.

Thousands of generations of man have been nourished, then, on the grass of the field. This should be enough to convince the most skeptical mind that the grasses must surely contain the essential chemicals (called nutrients) needed for life and health.

CHLOROPHYLL, BLOOD OF THE PLANT

Let us look deeply into the incredible engineering inherent in the Creation. The chlorophyll in the grass is the **blood** of the plant. It is made from the soil, air, water, and the sun.

Chlorophyll is the plant's source of life — without it, no plant survives. You can witness for yourself that without sunlight, air, and water, the leaves of all plants turn yellow, then brown, then they die.

Now, consider this carefully: it is the **blood of the plant** that gives life to the creatures that feed on it and it is the **light of the earth** (sunlight) that is required to make chlorophlyll.

LIFE THROUGH BLOOD

But this is just half of God's marvelous provision of redemption through blood. There's a principle beginning to take shape here that has me really excited. Let's continue with an analogy.

Just as the blood of the plant (chlorophyll) is its life, the blood of man is also his life. This is well-documented, both in Scripture and by science. But let's take an even closer look at the design of the Creator.

How does man get his blood? A recent discovery gives a more complete answer than ever before. I am so excited to be able to share this knowledge with you!

The molecular structure of the basic unit of blood in the plant (chlorophyll) is *almost the same* as the molecular structure of the basic unit of blood of man (hemoglobin) *except for the center atom.* The center atom in the plant is magnesium and for hemoglobin it is iron.

Now listen to this: when man eats green plants, **The blood molecule of the plant can become the blood molecule of man** by a process biochemists could not describe until recently. It is called porphyrin biosynthesis.

This, then, is the clincher of this unique story about blood. God in His marvelous wisdom provided perfectly for the self-repairing, self-rejuvenating, and self-energizing of the physical man through the blood of plants. God also provided perfectly for the repairing, rejuvenating, and energizing of man's spirit — through the blood of Jesus Christ.

BLOOD FROM LIGHT

It takes the **light of the earth** (the sun) to make the blood of the plant for the life and health of the physical man; and it takes **the light of the world (Jesus Christ)** who shed His blood to give life and health to the spiritual man. Both of these are fully and freely provided by our God, the Creator and Sustainer of the Universe.

REDEMPTION BY THE BLOOD

Why, then, are we such a sick people, full of physical ailments and diseases? And why are we, as a nation, forgetting our spiritual roots in government, education, agriculture, family life, and almost every profession you can name? The answer in truth is so simple.

Collectively and as individuals, **we have not applied "the blood"** to our lives. In the physical realm, we have abandoned a healthy diet where fresh green plants abound; instead we are eating skeletonized, dead, drugged, embalmed, coal-tarred, waxed, sprayed, irradiated, impure, and "forbidden by God" foods. In the spiritual realm, we are also consuming a nearly worthless diet, often stale and without substance.

We must return to our heritage in both realms, for **there is no other plan of salvation.**

CHAPTER SIX

A NEW PROVISION:
Green Barley, a Food with Real Power

Now that we have studied the spiritual roots of barley, let us apply what we have learned to green barley, the spray-dried juice of the green leaves of barley. It is really quite simple to make this application. On the personal level, the basic issue is this: are you interested in putting yourself, body, mind, and soul, in line with God's design?

I believe you are, because it is very unlikely that you would ever have picked up this book if you weren't. You have done your best, I would think, to get your mind and spirit renewed in God's Word, in good teaching, and in prayer. Now God is offering us a new food concentrate made from barley as a way of getting our bodies in line with His design for perfect health. That food is green barley, and I want to share with you some very specific reasons why it is so powerful.

SICKNESS AND HEALTH: SPIRITUAL WARFARE ON THE CELLULAR LEVEL

I assume that believers know that there is spiritual warfare going on at all times in this earth. If you have not become convinced of that, have a closer look at what Scripture has to say about Satan and his ministry.

In the tenth chapter of the Gospel of John, Jesus compares Himself to the Good Shepherd and tells us:

"The thief cometh not, but for to steal, and to kill, and to destroy: I am come that they might have life, and that they might have it more abundantly" (John 10:10).

Paul's letter to the Ephesians tells of a constant struggle in the natural realm between the forces of life and death:

"Put on the whole armour of God, that ye may be able to stand against the wiles of the devil. For we wrestle not against flesh and blood, but against principalities, against powers, against the rulers of the darkness of this world, against spiritual wickedness in high places" (Ephesians 6:11,12).

There has been a growing burden on my heart

that the forces of death have been making great strides in the area of what Americans accept as ***food.*** This concern began years ago.

As a university professor of Foods and Nutrition, I kept my eye on many different statistics having to do with lifestyle and health. It kept bothering me that the statistics on degenerative disease were constantly climbing. I noticed that diseases involving the immune system (like arthritis and cancer) were increasing alarmingly. All this, in our so-called "progressive" modern society ...?! What kind of "progress" is it that kills and disables at such a rate?

While the pollution of our air and water was getting most of the blame, along with the increased presence of toxic chemicals in the food chain, I had another idea. I kept wondering about the role of the vast changes in our eating habits and in the nutritional quality of the food available to us.

Dr. Hagiwara, the Japanese doctor who developed the process for low-temperature extraction of the concentrate from the green leaves of barley, expressed how I felt in his book, *Green Barley Essence.*

> *"... it was not until the 20th century that we have begun to mix chemical processing and food production, and it was not until we began to refine and process the nutrients out of our foods that new diseases began to appear. "[1]*

'NUTRITIONALLY DEAD' FOOD AND DEGENERATIVE DISEASE

While no single process or additive is likely to endanger health, today there are more than 7,500 chemical additives used in our foods. Every bit of processed food we eat has been treated with one or more of the following: bleaches, dyes, antioxidants, emulsifiers, preservatives, artificial flavors, enhancers, sweeteners, buffers, acidifiers, curing agents, alkalizers, deodorants, moisturizers, dessicants, defoliants, fungicides, neutralizers, thickeners, extenders, artificial sex hormones, disinfectants, anticaking and antifoaming agents, conditioners, antibiotics, hydrogenators, hydrolyzers, hydrogenated oils, arsenic, maturers, fortifiers, and pesticides.

All are added with the BOTTOM LINE in mind: PROFIT. They are in your food to extend its shelf life, make it more attractive visually, or make it taste, smell, or feel "just like the real thing" when the real thing is either unavailable or unprofitable. What has not been considered in most cases is the impact of these additives on the health of the consumer.

Let me state it in the boldest terms: **all of these additives are "dead" nutritionally;** some of them are just plain poison. Many of them render the foods to which they are added nutritionally useless. In fact, let me make a profound statement: in my view, **dead food makes dead people!**

On top of that, there is the continuing nutritional hazard posed by our national preference for cooked food. There are several reasons this is a problem, not the least of which is that cooking destroys the live enzymes in food, which God put there to fortify our bodies' defenses.

Not only that, but recent research indicates that a diet high in cooked foods causes more weight gain than the same diet where many of the foods are eaten raw. This fact alone helps explain why 65 percent of the American adult population is over-weight. We like most of our foods *well-cooked.* I often think of a relative who snipped the green beans first thing after breakfast and cooked them with plenty of salt pork 'til lunchtime! (Incidentally, I remember also that those little demons would *back-fire* until suppertime — or even until bedtime!)

When you consider that even our so-called "fresh" foods have been factory-farmed on depleted soils with artificial fertilizers, picked green (unripe), force-ripened, coated, canned, frozen, refined, chemi-cally processed, and/or warehoused for months, you can see why I was (and continue to be) increas-ingly alarmed about the "deadness" of our food supply.

Whatever you put inside your body is what your cells must use for energy, building blocks, or repair. If it cannot be used for any of these, it must be eliminated from your system. And if you have put a harmful or poisonous substance into your body, your defenses must be mobilized (at considerable expenditure of energy on the cellular level) to protect your body against its effects. **If the rate of harmful input exceeds the capacity of the body's defenses, you get degenerative disease.** And degenerative disease, left to its own devices, brings death.

LIFE FROM LIFE

Now you begin to see why my alarm system was being activated. God designed our bodies "fearfully and wonderfully" to sustain life from life, especially from live (raw) green plants. If the enemy of our souls can get us caught up in the effort to sustain life from dead food and toxic chemicals, of course he'll be just delighted.

I think the devil laughs every time he can deceive one of us into a soft-drink habit or jolly someone into believing that good nutrition is unimportant.

Have you ever noticed how much more the devil can accomplish through the affliction of degenerating health than by outright destruction? A standard tactic in warfare is to wound rather than kill, because killing takes only one soldier out of action. Wounding takes that soldier out of action plus at least two others to drag him off the field and likely several more to care for him.

God desires your health and strength so that you can be a witness to His salvation through Christ Jesus, and so that you can take your part in the battle against evil that we must wage in this earth. He has provided you with a body that can renew and protect itself. He has provided certain green plants to sustain these processes of renewal and protection. And, as we saw in Genesis 1:29, He even commanded us to eat them!

OBEDIENCE, SELF-DENIAL & SACRIFICE

There is one crucial factor in this positive cycle which only you can provide: obedience. And obedience almost always requires self-denial! Our ways are not usually His ways.

As we offer ourselves to Him through faith in the Gospel, a living sacrifice of praise and obedience, we invoke and activate the power of God on our behalf. This is just what the priests of ancient Israel attempted to do on behalf of the people. Every spring they offered up the perfect sheaf of barley, a sacrificial symbol of new life, of perfection and power.

What they had for a few fleeting moments every year, we have in Christ for eternity. We have confidence that our obedience through Christ will bear much fruit. Let us now take that obedience one step further and make barley our "bread." I believe the green leaves of barley is the ideal **live food** provided by God in answer to the **dead food** problem of our day and nation.

It really excites me to see the way God has designed this food in the most minute biochemical detail to restore, protect, and empower us to achieve His purpose for us — bringing His Life and Light into a dark and dying world.

ACTIVATING GOD'S POTENTIAL WITHIN

In the beginning, God designed our bodies to be self-rejuvenating, self-energizing, and self-renewing. The design hasn't changed. Even after the fall of Adam and Eve brought death into the world, it is still a spiritual malady (sin), not a physical one, that causes death.

Here's a crucial factor: to operate in the self-renewing mode, your body **must be nourished with what God intended you to eat!** As we saw in Genesis 1:29; 2:7, man was made from the "dust of the earth" and was to be nourished by green plants taken directly from the earth. Nothing else will meet our needs as well. Nothing at all! It is my belief that scientists will never disprove this concept.

We saw in the chapter on redemption how the Lord designed the molecules of chlorophyll and hemoglobin in perfect congruence for the building of blood. So it shouldn't come as a complete surprise that there are many other provisions for our health and the renewing of our cells built right into the cells of the young barley plant. Even if the dried concentrate of green leaves of barley *merely* corrected our dietary deficiency in the area of leafy greens, it would be worth more than its price. But there is so much more!

Let's take a short detour into the development of the product from barley leaves called Barley Green. Dr. Hagiwara made two important discoveries when he began looking for the ideal food supplement to help him regain his lost health. (Read the story in his book, *Green Barley Essence).*

THE DISCOVERY OF GREEN BARLEY

First, after testing dozens of different plants, he found the leaves of the "embryonic barley plant" — barley grass at between 10 and 12 inches high — held the most perfect balance of nutrients to be found in a group of more than 200 plants tested.

Second, he found a way to process the extracted juice of these leaves so that the living essences would not be destroyed. You have probably heard how various vitamins can be destroyed by heat. Well, green barley leaves have many natural vitamins, but the real "payload" of young barley grass is the rich concentration of live enzymes. These are even easier to destroy than vitamins.

Dr. Hagiwara invented a method of drying the fresh juice of barley leaves by injecting it in a fine spray through a vacuum chamber. This produces a fine powdered concentrate in a matter of seconds, and the temperature never gets over 97° F. This is well below the 107° F known as the beginning point for enzyme destruction.

The resulting green powder, with the addition of tiny amounts of powdered kelp and brown rice, is what you see when you open a jar of Barley Green. This vacuum-dried concentrate has a shelf life of approximately three years if protected from heat, light, and air.

According to Dr. Hagiwara, the reconstituted juice will actually begin to photosynthesize on your window sill if you set a glass of it there any time within that time frame. This is because of the biological activity within the chlorophyll molecule.

A NEW PROVISION

This new food concentrate from the green leaves of barley comes at a time when God's provision is sorely needed in our country. There is nothing new about it in terms of God's design, for we have seen that it was His intention from the beginning that our bodies be renewed through food from the earth, containing all the elements from which we are made. What is new and exciting is that the juice from young barley grass is now in a form that is accessible to us all! In fact, it is in **instant food** form.

Is it *merely a coincidence* that the conditions that have NO medical cure are the ones each of us can and must take personal responsibility for preventing? The tragedy of degenerative disease is that the conditions which are so often fatal by the time they require attention from a doctor are the very same conditions that are almost entirely preventable through a personal commitment to obeying God's plan for our health and healing through the foods He designed for our renewal.

We are to be living sacrifices, Paul tells us in the first two verses of Romans 12. Think about it: the basic requirement for a sacrifice is perfection, isn't it? I believe God intends for our health to be just that — perfect! And how fortunate we are that God provides the way whenever He asks us to obey.

OBEDIENCE AND REDEMPTION OF A HEATHEN KING

In the book of Daniel, we find a story about obedience. Nebuchadnezzar, king of Babylon, learns that obeying and honoring God in everything is the way to health, peace, and power in his life. Of course, he has to learn the hard way, but God made sure his story came down to us, so we wouldn't have to. What can we learn about the application of spiritual principles to our daily lives through his experience?

Daniel 4 is a story within a story. Complete in this chapter, we learn of King Nebuchadnezzar's frightening dream, Daniel's interpretation with its warning, the fulfillment of the dream, and the king's restoration by God after seven years of madness. Take a few moments right here to read the fourth chapter of Daniel, then we will look at it together.

In the first three verses of chapter four, King Nebuchadnezzar greets us with the high praises of God, declaring that he has a story to tell that will *"show the signs and wonders that the high God hath wrought toward me."*

We find the king has had another frightening and mystifying dream, with a vision he can't shrug off. His astrologers and magicians can't make anything of it, so Daniel, the prophet of God, is called in.

Nebuchadnezzar tells Daniel his dream vision, and at first Daniel is so taken aback by the dream and its meaning that he can't speak of it. *"Then Daniel was greatly perplexed for a time, and his thoughts alarmed him"* (Daniel 4:19 NIV). Finally, at the king's urging, Daniel answers and says:

> *"This is the interpretation, O king, and this is the decree of the most High, which is come upon my lord the king: That they shall drive thee from men, and thy dwelling shall be with the beasts of the field, and they shall make thee to eat grass as oxen, and*

*they shall wet thee with the dew of heaven, and
seven times shall pass over thee, till thou know that
the most High ruleth in the kingdom of men, and
giveth it to whomsoever he will" (Daniel 4:24,25).*

NEBUCHADNEZZAR REAPS THE CONSE-
QUENCES OF PRIDE & DISOBEDIENCE

One year later, we find King Nebuchadnezzar
walking about in his palace, saying, *"Is not this great
Babylon, that I have built ... by the might of my
power, and for the honur of my majesty?" (Daniel
4:30).* With that, there comes a voice from heaven,
and all that he had seen in the vision is fulfilled. He
is driven from the palace and for seven years he lived
in the fields and *"did eat grass as oxen, and his body
was wet with the dew of heaven" (Daniel 4:33).*

Let's pause and consider the king's predicament.
He had fallen into the hands of a God who keeps his
Word, and had given perfectly adequate warning of
what would happen if the king persisted in disobe-
dient ways. But Nebuchadnezzar continued in his
pride of doing things his own way and taking credit
to himself, and found himself at odds with God.

There are so many warnings in Scripture that
sound a lot like what God told Nebuchadnezzar
through Daniel. One paraphrase might be: "Do it my
way and live in peace; or do it your own way and
reap the consequences of disobedience. "

In this case, as in so many today, Nebuchadnezzar's consequences were also the source of a new-
found respect for God and His ways. How many of
us have had to be brought low by some debilitating
condition of body or mind, before we acknowledge
God's total sovereignty? Yet the warnings are there.
They've been there all along. Why wait to be brought
low when God is so willing to spell it out for us?

"Be not deceived; God is not mocked: for what-
soever a man soweth, that shall he also reap. For he
that soweth (junk food and pop) to his flesh shall of
the flesh reap corruption; but he that soweth (obedience) to the Spirit shall of the Spirit reap life everlast-
ing." (Galatians 6:8) (Words in parentheses added).

But Nebuchadnezzar had fallen into the mercy of
God, as well as His judgment, and came out of his
time of trial in better shape than when he went into
it. Daniel 4:34 says, *"And at the end of the days I
Nebuchadnezzar lifted up mine eyes unto heaven,
and mine understanding returned unto me, and I
blessed the most High, and I praised and honored
Him that liveth forever, whose dominion is an ever-
lasting dominion, and His kingdom is from generation to generation."*

NEBUCHADNEZZAR AND 'THE CURE'

Nebuchadnezzar had a health problem; not physical (as far as we know), but mental. But God wanted to use him, so God made sure he was cured. He

undertook to teach, heal and claim Nebuchadnez-zar as one of His own. When God got through with him, he was cured, in fact *"transformed by the re-newing of (his) mind" (Romans 12:1).*

Nebuchadnezzar's problem happened to be the pride of might, but many of us who are not kings have similar problems: we try to accomplish in our own strength what we are given to do. How often do we see that we have brought about our own trials and times of testing this way? But God is mighty to bring good even out of situations we bring upon ourselves by our own willfulness.

Let's just suppose, for a moment, Nebuchadnez-zar had heeded Daniel's warning in Daniel 4:27a: *"Wherefore, O king, let my counsel be acceptable unto thee, and break off thy sins by righteousness...."* If the king had turned from his heedless and God-dishonoring ways, he could have received a great blessing from God—seven years of learning the hard way would have become just totally unnecessary!

CHRONIC DISEASE AND 'LEARNING THE HARD WAY'

I believe that many of the chronic diseases we are seeing today that have no real cure and that may be caused or triggered by stress, are examples of "learn-ing the hard way." Let us then heed what God has to say about the way He wants us to live.

We are to praise and honor Him, as Nebuchad-nezzar found out, and to acknowledge His dominion in every area of our lives. I believe that when we start letting God have dominion over our diet and nutrition, we will see a dramatic decrease in chronic unwellness of all kinds. We simply won't have to be "learning the hard way!"

Now let's look at one aspect of the story that is seldom considered: the king's diet. What did Scripture say he ate during those seven years? Grass! This is a very foreign concept to Americans. (It has been said that we are the only country in the world that harvests a crop every week, but never eats it!) Obviously, this is not a recommendation that we eat our lawn clippings. But it does have meaning for us in a larger sense.

GREEN PLANTS AND HEALTH

If you go back to the first chapter of Daniel, you will find that one of the sources of the surpassing excellence of Daniel's witness was his diet. He and his companions refused to eat "the king's meat" because many of the dishes offered were not in line with the dietary laws God had given the Hebrews through Moses.

Daniel convinced the king's steward to try them for ten days on just vegetables and water (Daniel 1:12). At the end of the time, the steward's skepticism was overcome by the healthy appearance of Daniel and his companions, surpassing even those who had a far "richer" diet.

Clearly, both in this story and in the story of Nebuchadnezzar's seven years of eating grass, God is showing us that He will bless those who honor Him. But I believe He is also telling us something very specific about diet and health. We saw in Genesis that God was quite particular to specify His food plan. We are to find nourishment primarily from green plants, cereals, nuts, seeds, and fruits.

GOD TEACHES US WHAT NOT TO EAT

Nebuchadnezzar had spent his life eating "rich" foods — meat is mentioned, very likely plenty of pork and lamb, valued because it had lots of fat. Fat meat is more pleasing to the sense of smell and taste, but it is not according to God's plan for us to overeat meat and other fatty foods.

In Leviticus 7:23, God tells Moses, *"Speak unto the children of Israel, saying, Ye shall eat no manner of fat, of ox, or of sheep, or of goat."*

Again in Proverbs 23:20, God warns his people, *"Be not among winebibbers; among riotous eaters of flesh."*

Wine is also part of "the king's table" (Daniel 1:8); it is entirely possible that King Nebuchadnezzar had become, if not an alcoholic, perhaps a borderline abuser of wine. His metabolism may have been so clogged up that God knew it would take seven years of "detoxification" just to get through to him!

GREEN BARLEY AS A DETOXIFIER

It is interesting to note that green barley is being used very successfully as a detoxifier in the treatment of alcoholics.[2] It is quite possible that Nebuchadnezzar's judgment and ability to rule were becoming impaired by overconsumption of alcohol. God's cure is worth careful consideration.

In our discussion of cell selection, we noted the incredible wisdom that God built into our cells when He designed them: to choose the highest quality nutrients available to them at any given point in time, and eliminate the poorer quality substances. This means, in the case of problems like alcoholism, that the body has large quantities of toxins and toxic by-products to process out of the system; high quality nutrients like the ones found in green barley initiate and support this detoxification process.

Many of us who would never consider polluting our bodies with drugs such as alcohol consume large quantities of caffeine, nitrites and nitrates, phosphoric acid (soft drinks) and sugar. The same process of detoxification must occur to remove these hazardous and stressful substances from our cells and rebuild from high quality nutrients.

Remember, God designed our bodies to be nourished from the earth of which they were originally composed. In these times, He has provided a **fast food** made from barley leaves to remedy the lack of nourishing vegetable foods available and to bring us back into line with His plan for our ongoing health. Let's honor Him in our diet just as in other areas of our lives — that way we can avoid having to learn "the hard way!"

GOD'S PROVISION IN GREEN BARLEY

I have been truly blessed by this opportunity to share what I have learned and what I believe God has shown me, both in my work as a nutritionist and in my experience with His mighty compassion and provision for us. My hope is that you have been blessed and will continue your pursuit of health and healing according to God's design and provision.

FOOTNOTES

[1] Yoshihide Hagiwara, M.D., *Green Barley Essence,* Keats Publishing, Inc., New Canaan, CT, 1985.

[2] Edward Howell, *Enzyme Nutrition,* Avery Publishing Group, Inc., Wayne, NJ, 1985

Want to know more?

Write to Dr. Swope at: **NUTRITION WITH A MISSION,**
P.O. Box 1746, MELBOURNE, FL 32902 • 407-951-7765

BOOKS BY DR. SWOPE

GREEN LEAVES OF BARLEY: A FOOD WITH REAL POWER . $7

ARE YOU SICK & TIRED OF FEELING SICK & TIRED?....... $5

NUTRITION FOR CHRISTIANS $6

LISTENING PRAYER $7

THE SPIRITUAL ROOTS OF BARLEY $5

A Cookbook, by JoAnn Rachor
OF THESE YE MAY FREELY EAT $3.50

CASSETTE TAPES BY DR. SWOPE

S.W. RADIO CHURCH: #1   (Good nutrition); $4
                         #2   (Green barley); $4
                         #3   (Eat Yourself Healthy) $4
NUTRITION TEACHING — Tabernacle Church (two tapes) $6

VIDEO TAPES WITH DR. SWOPE

DARBRO/SWOPE — Nutrition Update $20
SWOPE/McKEEVER — It's Not Too Late: a nutrition update $29
SWOPE/McKEEVER — Using Nutrition as Medicine $29

GREEN BARLEY PRODUCT INFORMATION .... no charge
DISTRIBUTOR INFORMATION PACKET (1 TO A CUSTOMER) $1

SUB TOTAL: _____
SALES TAX — FLORIDA RESIDENTS (6%) _____

Shipping & Handling Schedule:
     $2-$10 Add $1; $10.01- $30 Add $2; $30.01 to $50 Add $3   _____

TOTAL: _____

NAME ....

ADDRESS ....

CITY/STATE/ZIP ....

PHONE ....